INVENTORS & IMPOSTORS

INVENTORS & IMPOSTORS

HOW HISTORY FORGOT THE TRUE HEROES OF INVENTION AND DISCOVERY

Daniel Diehl and Mark P Donnelly

crimson

This edition first published in Great Britain 2008 by
Crimson Publishing, a division of Crimson Business Ltd
Westminster House
Kew Road
Richmond
Surrey
TW9 2ND

A catalogue record for this book is available from the British library.

ISBN 978 1 90587 907 6

Typeset by 4word Ltd, Bristol
Printed and bound in the UK by MPG Books Ltd, Bodmin, Cornwall

'These are facts, historical facts, not schoolbook history, not Mr Wells' history, but history nevertheless.'
Dashiell Hammett, *The Maltese Falcon*

'Sacred cows make the best burgers if you grind them up just right.'
Reverend Billy C Wirtz

The Big Book of Pain – Torture and punishment
through history
Management Secrets from History
Eat Thy Neighbour – A history of cannibalism
Tales from the Tower of London
Elbert Hubbard – The commonsense revolutionary
How Did They Manage? – Leadership secrets of history
Medieval Furniture – Plans & instructions
Medieval Celebrations
Siege – Castles at war
Constructing Medieval Furniture

Table of Contents

Introduction

There is an oft-quoted truism that non-fiction writers, much like teachers, collect more information than they can possibly pass on to their audience. Never was this more the case than in the writing of this book. When our publisher asked us to write a book about forgotten or overlooked inventors and discoverers, we thought it sounded like a grand idea. We also thought that, as experienced writers and historians, the project would be relatively straightforward. How wrong we were! Every piece of research led to another, and that one to yet another, and so on. It was rather like opening a series of Russian dolls, or unravelling a gigantic ball of string. For example, we simply had no idea how many common-place machines and devices that we not only took for granted, but also assumed we knew something about, were actually the result of years, decades and sometimes even centuries of one individual after another building on (and sometimes, it seemed, blatantly co-opting) the ideas of other people. It was a fascinating, and intriguing, tour of received wisdom, urban myth and human nature.

Much of what you will read in this book may strike you as astounding, if not downright unbelievable. Some of the people we have been brought up to believe were clever, if not brilliant, heroes of science, invention and discovery were, in fact, simply brilliant self-promoters (or had deeper financial pockets, better connections or firmer luck). Of course, this was not true in every case, but it seemed to have happened often enough to shake our confidence in much of what we had been taught, or at least to doubt that we had been given the full picture. As a result, the information contained in these pages (which has been put into chronological order, according to our identification of an invention or discovery) will probably never make it into textbooks or onto the school curriculum; after all, history is written by the winners. It is in this sense, perhaps, that many of these individuals could be considered 'impostors' – not that they deliberately set out to deceive, but that their place in history has been overstated.

This book may raise some debate; it may raise some awkward questions. But debate and questioning are always worthwhile.

Experience shows that history is rarely black and white; this book dares to explore the shadows.

We very much hope that you enjoy reading this book. We also hope that, while we cannot claim to have covered every single event or contribution, you come away with a greater understanding of how the inventions and discoveries that helped shape our modern world came to pass.

Finally, if there is one lesson to be learned from these tales, it is that, when it comes to history, as with so much we are taught in life, we must be cautious, diligent and willing to question everything.

Daniel Diehl and Mark P Donnelly

1

Christopher Columbus & the Discovery of America

'In fourteen-hundred-and-ninety-two Columbus sailed the ocean blue'.

Until relatively recent times, every American school child first learned about the discovery of their country with a little rhyme beginning with this line. Up to this point, of course, the rhyme is unquestionably accurate. In the summer of that year Christopher Columbus did indeed sail westward from Spain and land on what is now the island of San Salvador. In total, he made four trips to the New World, the last concluding in 1504. What Columbus did *not* do, however, was set foot on mainland North America. That honour would be reserved for English explorer John Cabot (who, incidentally, was Italian by birth), and took place in 1497. So why is Columbus so revered?

According to popular lore, Columbus, a crack navigator from Genoa in Italy, spent years convincing King Ferdinand II of Aragon and Queen Isabella of Castile to finance a voyage westward to discover a water route from Europe to China and India. With the overland trade routes controlled by the Moors (Arabs), and the sea route around Africa controlled by the Portuguese, direct, free access to the spice and silk trade would vastly increase Spain's wealth, power and influence among its European neighbours. As the tale goes, Ferdinand and Isabella finally agreed; the Queen pawned her jewels to raise cash and Columbus made the perilous journey with a fractious, superstitious crew who threatened revolt at every turn. In the end, the intrepid captain returned home with tidings of a new land and everyone lived happily ever after.

Seldom mentioned is the fact that by 1492 nearly every educated person knew the true circumference of the Earth (which had been accurately calculated as early as the second century BC), and that no ship could possibly make the trip Columbus proposed without running out of food and water. Columbus, on the other hand, miscalculated the length of his proposed trip by some 4,000 nautical miles. Had the Western Hemisphere not gotten in his way, Columbus and his men would undoubtedly have perished. Columbus never admitted to the mistake and insisted to his dying day that he had reached islands lying off the east coast of Asia. But does this miscalculation take anything away from Columbus' accomplishments? It does, if Captain Columbus knew a lot more than he ever told his royal sponsors.

Until the advent of modern navigational aids, no sailor willingly sailed at night through strange waters. The danger of hidden shoals and reefs, and the vagaries of the weather, made such actions too dangerous to risk. Columbus, however, sailed both day and night. In fact, according to his chronicler, Las Casas, during his first voyage Columbus sailed over 300 miles more during night hours than he did during the day. If the waters through which he was moving were as completely unknown as is widely believed, why would a supposedly experienced captain take such a gamble? The answer, of course, is because he had prior knowledge. But how could Columbus have obtained this precious information?

According to the biography written by Columbus' son, Ferdinand, the elder Columbus had done his homework. In 1477 he had travelled to Iceland where he met with the local bishop who described a vast western land mass, known to the Nordic inhabitants of Iceland and Greenland as 'Vinland'. We will come back to the Icelandic connection a bit later, but for now let us confine ourselves to what Columbus knew, and how he came to know it.

A sure way to uncover corporate secrets is to marry into the family, and this is precisely what Columbus did in 1479. His wife, Filipa de Perestrello, was the daughter of the Governor of the Portuguese-owned Madeira Islands, and daddy was well connected at court. Through the Governor's good graces, Columbus managed to obtain access to Portuguese naval information. Known as the 'Portuguese Rudder', one folio contained top-secret naval maps, tide charts, latitude readings and details of land masses for virtually the entire Atlantic Ocean.

Then there is the case of a map drawn in 1489 by Henricus Martellus (a Latinized version of Heinrich Hammer), a highly respected late medieval German scholar. Two copies of Martellus' map still exist – one in the British Library and the other in the library of the University of Leiden. It is a map of the coast of South America, with the main rivers so closely drawn that at least two of them were not confirmed until the late 19th century. While this map languished, nearly forgotten, for centuries, it was well known in its day. It seems inconceivable that, given his lengthy quest for information on what lay across the great 'Ocean Sea' (as the Atlantic was then known), Columbus would have failed to have discovered its existence and consulted it. But where did the information on Martellus' map come from?

It is common knowledge that Columbus made unsuccessful attempts to secure backing for his venture from several governments in his native Italy, as well as from the Portuguese, long before he convinced Ferdinand and Isabella to part with their cash and three well-worn ships. Could it be that these countries turned him down because they already knew exactly what he would find out there?

For nearly a century before Columbus' time the Portuguese had maintained an iron grip on shipping lanes in the mid-Atlantic and around Africa, and this had allowed them to monopolize the European spice and silk trade. Obviously, they kept their naval charts, such as the Portuguese Rudder, secret; to divulge what they knew would have levelled the playing field and threatened their unassailable position in trade. A Portuguese map of 1424 (not generally known until it was published by Portugal's Coimbra University in 1954) revealed a far greater knowledge of the Atlantic region than most of Europe possessed a century later. Building on this knowledge, Portugal's fine, swift fleet of caravel ships expanded their explorations until, by 1502 (as shown on the still-surviving 'Cantino' map of that year), Portuguese navigators had a detailed understanding not only of such diverse places as Newfoundland and the West Indies (which Columbus had 'discovered' only 10 years earlier) but also of the Florida Peninsula. In a 1992 television documentary, the German ZDF network displayed maps from the collection of the Portuguese National Archives in Lisbon that clearly revealed a detailed knowledge of the North American coastline long before Columbus' time. There is, in fact, both contemporary ships' log entries and archaeological evidence to show that the Portuguese had landed at Dighton Rocks near Taunton, Massachusetts decades before Columbus stumbled his way onto San Salvador.

But to find out who got there before the Portuguese, let us return to the Icelandic settlements visited by Columbus in 1477. Looking at a map of the North Atlantic, it is obvious that Iceland is only half way between Scandinavia and Canada; but that puts it a whole lot closer to the New World than either Spain or Portugal. The people of Iceland were then (as they are now) of Nordic stock, and have been living on their forbiddingly cold island since late in the ninth century. How did they travel so far so long ago? They were Vikings.

Long before the first Portuguese caravel put to sea, Viking long-boats were plying the waters of the world in search of trade and plunder. In addition to harrying England and France unmercifully during the late Dark Ages, the Vikings travelled to Byzantium (modern Turkey) and to what are now Russia and Iran. In the year 860 they landed on, and settled, Iceland, and in 982 that intrepid, ginger-bearded Norseman, Erik the Red, sailed even further west to the impossibly inhospitable Greenland, where his son, Leif Erikson, eventually established a colony.

According to Viking saga, both Leif and fellow venturer Bjarni Herjolfson soon made their way even closer to mainland Canada, to a place which they called 'Vinland'; but neither was particularly impressed with what they found. Their followers, however, returned to the outlying Canadian islands some time in the 12th or 13th century and founded ill-fated colonies which collapsed due to the hostile climate.

Early Viking exploration of Iceland and Greenland has never been in dispute. Even scholars as respected as Adam of Bremen (Adamus Bremensis) stated in his book on the Christianization of Europe (written around 1075) that the Norwegians knew of land beyond Greenland which they called 'Vinland the Good'. The problem in establishing Vinland as being North

America proper lay in the fact that the Viking sagas, which told of this place, were handed down by oral tradition, and therefore subject to change and alteration over centuries of retelling. However, in the 19th century, Arctic explorer Charles Francis Hall led an expedition to Kodlunarn Island in Frobisher Bay, in Canada's Labrador Sea, where his team discovered an iron 'bloom' – waste material from an early medieval iron-smelting furnace. Additional blooms were discovered in 1981 by a Smithsonian expedition to the same site, and were dated as being from either the 12th or 13th century. In 1961 the remains of primitive house foundations were found at L'Anse aux Meadows in northern Newfoundland. Mixed among the rubble were Norse spindle whorls (weights from a spindle used for spinning woollen thread) that dated from around the year 1000 AD. Apparently, by cross-referencing details given in the Viking sagas with discoveries made in north-eastern Canada, the Viking colonies of Helluland and Markland can be identified as Baffin Island and Labrador respectively. Exactly which part of Canada was originally dubbed Vinland remains vague.

The trouble is, of course, that even the Vikings may not have made it all the way to mainland North America, but as it seems Columbus never did either, their claim to discovering America is just as valid as his, and predates him by half a millennium.

There is a long-debated legend, based on ancient Welsh sagas, that in or around the year 1170 a Welsh prince named Madoc (Madog) made incursions into

North America proper. According to the saga, Madoc, who was Wales' most skilled seaman, along with his brother Rhirid, set out in eight ships from the port of Abercerrig following a vitriolic dispute over the succession to their father's throne. Eventually, Madoc and Rhirid landed in what has tentatively been identified as the bay of Mobile, Alabama – which is both a very long way west, and an equally long way south, of Wales. Somehow the brothers made their way back home, spread the news of their discovery, rounded up a band of foolhardy volunteers, returned to establish a colony and promptly vanished.

The legend may well have died there had it not been that later explorers, both English and Spanish, reportedly discovered a tribe of Native Americans (who never seem to be credited with discovering America in the first place) with pale skin and who, believe it or not, spoke Welsh. Even such notables as the conquistador Hernán Cortéz attested to this fact; but how Cortéz could have recognized Welsh is never explained. What is indisputable is that in 1797 an English explorer of Welsh extraction, named John Evans, described spending years trying to find this tribe of 'Welsh Indians', now identified as the Mandans of the Upper Missouri region. In the end, Evans insisted that the whole thing was a fabrication, and the English and Welsh, in turn, denounced Evans as a spy for the Spanish. Sadly, the truth will never be known; the Mandans were wiped out by an epidemic of smallpox in 1838.

An equally unsupportable, but slightly less improbable, account of 'first contact' with the Americas comes from Chinese court records from the Leang Dynasty during the first half of the sixth century. According to the official chronicles, a group of sailors had been blown off course and travelled 5,000 miles (*c.*8,000 km) to the east where they discovered a land which they dubbed 'Tahan', or 'Great China'. Certainly the distance from China to the Aleutian Islands is about right, and if the sailors had been carried by the Japan Current of the Northern Pacific this is undoubtedly where they would have ended up. Unfortunately for the Chinese (like the Welsh), we lack hard, physical evidence for this feat. Some archaeologists claim a more than passing similarity between Chinese pottery of this period and similarly dated pots and bowls discovered in Ecuador, but a few pot shards do not a civilization make. Not to worry. There are far earlier, and better supported, claimants to the discovery of the New World than either the Welsh or the Chinese.

Around 330 BC a Greek traveller named Pytheas of Massilia wrote that he had travelled on a Phoenician ship when it visited a place he called 'Thule'. Pytheas could not identify Thule's location, but insisted it lay far beyond the Straits of Moloch (later known as the 'Pillars of Hercules', and now the Straits of Gibraltar); further from his homeland than any other place on Earth. He noted that the sea around its shores often became thick and congealed during the winter months. Presumably, this last was a reference to ice-bound sea lanes.

Outlandish as this account may sound, it is now, as it was then, widely acknowledged that the Phoenicians ranked among the finest sailors in history. Centuries before Christ, the Phoenicians had built ships that displaced more than 6,000 tonnes and which, according to the early Hebrew historian Flavius Josephus, were capable of carrying 600 passengers in addition to supplies and crew. The Greek historian Herodotus (484–425 BC) said that Phoenician galleys routinely sailed 70,000 fathoms (a fathom is equal to 6 feet or nearly 2 metres) during daylight hours and another 60,000 during darkness; about 150 miles (240 km) for every 24 hours of running time.

Employing their unparalleled naval skills, the Phoenicians (known as the 'Sea People' to virtually every civilization around the eastern rim of the Mediterranean) made forays into the unknown that would have been unthinkable to anyone else. From their home bases at Sidon and Tyre, located along the Mediterranean coast of what is now Lebanon, they routinely traded with the Egyptians, the Hebrews and the early Greeks, even travelling as far as the British Isles to trade for tin. They explored the entire north coast of Africa, establishing a colony at Carthage (in what is now Tunis) and another on the East African coast. By 2000 BC the Phoenicians were already the uncontested rulers of the seas. So great was their renown that around 1000 BC King Solomon asked King Hiram I of Tyre to send carpenters and sailors to help him build and navigate a fleet of ships that was to travel from Ezion-Geber, at the head of the Gulf of Akabah, to the land of Ophir, far to the south. Four centuries later, Pharaoh Necho II commissioned the Phoenicians to circumnavigate the African continent, and it may well have been this expedition which led to the establishment of the colony known as 'Zimbabwe' (incidentally, this is not the same place as the modern-day country, named in its honour).

But what have these extraordinary accomplishments to do with the discovery of the Americas? For centuries historians have argued that Thule was the Phoenician name for the Western Continent; but could their ships possibly have travelled from their westernmost port at Carthage all the way across the Atlantic?

Based on a speed of 150 miles per day (and making some allowance for tacking and the vagaries of currents), it would have taken them slightly more than six weeks of fair weather and steady winds to cover the nearly 5,000 miles from North Africa to the Brazilian coast, and only a month to reach Florida. According to Herodotus' description of their ships' capacity, they could certainly have carried sufficient supplies to make the journey without undue privation. In 1970, in an attempt to prove just such a possibility, Norwegian marine biologist Thor Heyerdahl set out from the Moroccan coast 900 miles (1,448 km) west of ancient Carthage (undoubtedly the Phoenicians' final anchorage prior to setting off into the unknown) in a boat made of reeds – *Ra II*, not the more famous

Kon-Tiki – and headed for the Americas. While he never made continental landfall, Heyerdahl did make it all the way to the Bahamas – and did so in only 57 days, thus proving his point admirably. Of course, the fact that the Phoenicians *could* have made such a journey is not proof that they actually did.

As we have seen, one of the Phoenicians' most profitable trading partners was Egypt, and surely whatever rare and exotic things the Phoenicians may have brought back from the Americas would have been snapped up by this, the richest country on Earth. Could the bounty of the Sea People's ships be the source for the nicotine residue found in Egyptian mummies that archaeologists and anthropologists have long puzzled over? Nicotine is unique to tobacco, and tobacco is native to the Americas. Additional evidence comes to us from archaeological excavations carried out by the French in 1860, at the ancient Phoenician city of Sidon, where a number of artifacts made of 'quebracho' wood were found. Quebracho only grows in the Brazilian rainforest. There is also a small mountain of Phoenician inscriptions that supports the supposed journeys to Thule. One such inscription is on a tombstone – now in the British Museum – which says (in part) that the deceased had been a sailor who travelled beyond the Straits of Moloch to Thule, 'where the sea penetrates into the land'. Evidence, perhaps, that this individual had been somewhere, but it fails to prove that Thule was America.

Other Phoenician inscriptions have a more direct bearing on the case. In the late 1960s archaeologists excavating the temple of Sechim in the Casma Valley along the Peruvian coast discovered carvings of a type of ship only known to have existed in ancient Phoenicia.

More astounding are the rock carvings which were discovered and photographed by Bernardo Silva Ramos, President of the Manaus Geographical Institute, back in the 1900s. Deep in the rainforests of the Amazon river basin, Ramos found more than 2,800 inscriptions, the vast majority of which were executed in Phoenician glyphs or Egyptian hieratic (a common-language variation of hieroglyphics). Part of one of these inscriptions reads: 'We are children of Canaan, from the city of Sidon. We are a nation of traders. Our ship is beached on this far-off mountainous coast and we make sacrifice to the gods and goddesses. In the 19th year of Hiram's reign we set sail from Ezion-Geber and crossed the Red Sea with 10 ships. We have been sailing now for two years and have sailed all around this land.'

It is worth noting that the Phoenicians' apparent port of departure is the same one mentioned in the Bible as being used by King Solomon, and it would appear that the king they specifically mention was most probably Hiram III, who reigned in the middle of the sixth century BC. Curiously, they also state that they left through the Red Sea, making it appear that, unless they rounded the Horn of Africa before sailing north and then westward, their chosen route from the Middle East to South America would have been around India and Indo-China, and then across the entire Pacific. This would certainly seem to be doing things the hard way, but it would account for the incised carvings of Phoenician ships being found in Peru, which is on South America's Pacific coast.

By now it would seem clear that, while Columbus may indeed have sailed the ocean blue in fourteen-hundred-and-ninety-two, he was doing little more than following in the wake of others who had ploughed the same route for more than 2,000 years. So why then did Columbus become inextricably linked with the discovery of America? Because in 1828 the immensely popular American writer, Washington Irving, author of *The Legend of Sleepy Hollow*, wrote a book entitled *The Life and Voyages of Christopher Columbus*. The book became a bestseller and the rest, as they say, is history.

2

James Watt & the Steam Engine

If you hear the words 'steam engine' the image which most likely comes to mind is that of a 19th or early 20th century railway locomotive. These were, of course, driven by steam, but throughout the 19th century steam powered nearly every large piece of machinery in every factory in the industrialized world. To those historically-minded individuals who are aware of this fact, the man they will credit with the creation of the stationary steam engine will most likely be James Watt. However, while Watt contributed significantly to the commercialization of the steam engine, he was not its creator. So what is a steam engine, and why is Watt's name so closely associated with it, the first viable, man-made power source?

Simply put, a steam engine is an external combustion engine in which a water-filled boiler is heated by fire. The boiling water produces steam which, in turn, drives a piston that provides motive power to run machinery. Watt's story is a bit more complicated.

James Watt was born in 1736 in Greenock, Scotland where his father was a ship builder, ship owner and sometime chief magistrate of the town. A bright but physically frail child, James was educated at home by his mother who encouraged his interest in small mechanical devices and mathematics.

When James was 18 his parents sent him to Glasgow to learn the trade of mathematical instrument-maker. There, his friend Dr Dick, of the University of Glasgow, advised James to go to London where he would be better able to learn his trade. Watt went as directed, but after a year ill-health forced him to return to Glasgow where he intended to set up his own shop. Despite being the only schooled mathematical instrument-maker in Scotland, Watt was denied permission to open a business because he had not completed a seven-year apprenticeship. Again, Dr Dick came to Watt's rescue by providing him with a shop on the university grounds where he could repair university equipment and still take in work from the public.

Some time around his fourth year in business, Watt began to read about, and experiment with, steam power. Despite never having seen a steam engine he repeatedly tried to build one. His success was limited to say the least. During the winter of 1763–64 Watt learned that the university's Natural Philosophy Department owned a working scale model of a steam engine designed 60 years earlier by a man named Thomas Newcomen, but that the machine had been sent to London for repairs. Watt begged university authorities to recall the device and give him a chance to make the necessary repairs himself. They agreed, but probably with some misgivings.

As well as whatever mechanical problems plagued the machine, Watt found himself confronted with a mechanism that was far from fuel efficient. According to his notes, Watt calculated that Newcomen's engine wasted 80% of its power through lost heat. Watt's first insight was to insulate the boiler to prevent heat loss. Next, realizing that steam stored far more heat than water, he devised a secondary chamber in which excess steam could be stored at a constant temperature. This steam reservoir provided extra power to drive the single piston that ran the water pump, for which Newcomen had originally devised his engine. In a little over a year, Watt had made far more improvements to the Newcomen engine than had been made in the six decades since its creation; he had also spent so much time perfecting the machine that he had neglected his other work and was, as a result, virtually destitute. Watt had already borrowed as much money as he could from his friends, had secured a patent, and now, on the brink of being able to commercialize the vastly improved steam engine, had no means of continuing his work. What he needed was investment capital. Step forward one Matthew Boulton.

Boulton was a wealthy foundry owner from Birmingham in the English Midlands who was always looking for innovative ways to make his foundry more efficient and, hopefully, more profitable in the process. In 1769 Boulton bought a share of Watt's patent and in 1775 formally set up Boulton & Watt, with Watt acting as manager. Now freed from monetary worries, Watt continued to improve the mechanics of the engine, specifically by finding a way to bore more efficient piston cylinders. By 1776 the first Boulton & Watt engines were ready to go on the market, and were quickly snapped up by mine owners who had been using the old Newcomen engines to pump accumulated water out of their deep-shaft mines. More pumps were installed at London's municipal waterworks.

All this was good for Boulton & Watt, but Watt's greatest contribution to the burgeoning Industrial Revolution was perhaps devising a way to convert the up-and-down force of the piston into the circular motion necessary to operate industrial machinery. To envision this transfer of power, think of the way in which a locomotive piston turns the wheels of an engine. A simple concept, but Watt was the first to commercialize it.

Over the years Watt devised innumerable improvements for the steam engine, including a 'governor' to keep the engine from running too fast which could, and sometimes did, result in the boiler exploding. By 1785 Watt had been elected a fellow of London's prestigious Royal Society, and his improved steam engine had almost completely replaced that of Thomas Newcomen. Thus did Watt's name outshine Newcomen's; but how did Newcomen come up with the idea? Or did it originate with him at all?

In the late 1600s and early 1700s Thomas Newcomen owned what we would think of today as an industrial-scale hardware store, scrapyard and machine shop. He not only sold machines and machine parts but, as the need arose, he also manufactured them. In 1698, at the age of 35, Newcomen entered a business partnership with Thomas Savery, an inventor who held several patents on a primitive steam engine that could be used to pump accumulated water out of mine shafts. Newcomen knew that keeping water seepage out of mines was an impossibly expensive process and that Savery's pumping engine was not really up to the job for which it was intended. Newcomen's variation on the Savery engine utilized a single steam-powered piston that worked not unlike a pump handle; as the piston moved up and down it sucked water out of the mine. By 1705 Newcomen had devised an 8 horsepower engine with an 8 inch (200 mm) diameter pump that could raise water a distance of 162 feet (almost 50 metres). Impressive, considering that this volume of water weighs 3,535 pounds (*c.*1,600 kg). What made the engine work as well as it did was Newcomen's use of a counterweight to help return the piston to the 'up' position once the steam pressure had driven it 'down'.

But like Watt, Newcomen was only improving on another man's invention; in this case, that of his business partner, Thomas Savery.

Savery, born in 1650 in Devonshire, England was a well-educated military engineer whose hobby was mechanics, mathematics and physics. As an engineer, Savery was well aware of the problems mining companies faced in keeping water from seeping into their mines, accumulating in the shafts and eventually flooding the system. Hauling the water out with horses was extremely expensive and time consuming. In large mines, up to 500 horses and their handlers were required to cart water out of the mine shafts. With this in mind, in the 1690s Savery began researching and working on a steam-powered pump that could draw water out of a mine shaft and lift it to the surface.

Savery's engine consisted of a large copper boiler in which steam was produced. The steam was forced up a pipe which was then closed at the bottom by turning off a valve, while another valve, attached to an adjoining pipe (the lower end of which was submerged in the accumulated water in the floor of the mine), was cranked open. The fire beneath the boiler was then extinguished, and as the boiler cooled a vacuum was created in the siphon pipe and the unwanted water was sucked toward the surface. Considering that Savery's pump had absolutely no moving parts, it probably worked as well as could be expected; at least it worked better than anything else available in the late 1690s. In 1698 Savery exhibited a working model of his pump before King William III (William III of Orange) at Hampton Court Palace; His Majesty was sufficiently impressed to immediately grant Savery a 14-year patent. The possible uses for this device must already have been apparent because the title of the patent paper reads 'A grant to Thomas Savery of the sole exercise of a new invention... for raising water... which will be of great use for draining mines, serving towns with water, and for the working of all sorts of mills when they have not the benefit of [flowing] water nor constant winds...'

Although the possibility of using steam as a motive power in factories and flour mills was obvious, Savery's engine was simply not up to the job. Its limited efficiency only allowed it to draw water to a height of about 30 feet (9 m), and without a piston there was no way to adapt even this limited power to machinery. Still, it did work, and was the first known machine used to pump water from mines.

Being a caring sort, and hoping to generate as much publicity as possible, Savery published a pamphlet in 1702 entitled *The Miner's Friend – Or, an engine to raise water by fire,* in which he extolled the virtues of his 'fire-powered' vacuum pump. He also exhibited a model before the Royal Society and presented it with a full set of plans and specifications. Savery's advertising campaign was a success. Savery engines were installed in mines, in towns and villages, and even in London, where they pumped water from public wells. On private estates, smaller pumps provided water for both the house and gardens. Unfortunately, while it did pump, the Savery engine was simply not capable of keeping ahead of water incursion in many mines. As already mentioned, Savery researched his subject well before embarking on his steam engine. In particular, he researched the work of a Frenchman named Denis Papin.

Papin, a physicist and mathematician, was born in Blois, France in 1647, only three years before Savery. After gaining a medical degree, Papin settled in Paris where he assisted the renowned Dutch mathematician Christiaan Huygens. After helping Huygens in his experiments with air pumps, Papin moved to London to become the assistant of mathematician and chemist Robert Boyle. While working with Boyle, Papin invented what he called his 'Steam Digester', an early form of pressure cooker. It was apparent that the pressure of steam made food cook faster, and Papin continued to experiment with steam after he left London in 1687 to assume the Chair of Mathematics at Marburg University in Germany. Here, in 1690, he was asked to devise an automatic water pump. Papin already knew that a very small amount of water – when converted to steam – could produce tremendous pressure. If this pressure could be made to work in reverse – to create a vacuum – it should be able to siphon water. He was, of course, quite right. Later that same year, after building a working model of his steam engine, Papin wrote up his findings in a paper called *'Nova Methodus ad Vires Motrices Validissimas Levi Pretio Comparandas'*. Translated from Latin, this reads 'A New Method of Securing Inexpensive Motive Power of Considerable Magnitude'.

What was new to Papin's engine was an enclosed firebox situated in the middle of a reservoir of water. It is the first known instance of this development, and one which increased the efficiency of the steam engine greatly by producing a pressure of up to 1,200 pounds (544 kg) per square inch. The Papin engine only produced about 1 horsepower's worth of energy, but its 2½ inch (63 mm) diameter cylinder could raise 60 pounds (27 kg) of water a minute. Despite its high cost and low efficiency, Papin sold more than 1,500 steam pumps. Interestingly, he also designed the first safety valve; an absolute necessity if this dangerously high-pressure system was not to explode. Even more interesting is that in 1705 Papin invented yet another steam engine, this one based on Thomas Savery's 1702 description of his own machine which had, in turn, been based on Papin's pressure cooker. For nearly 15 years these two men traded ideas back and forth, each building on the other's work, and apparently doing so without any rancour.

One of the things Papin had in common with Savery, Newcomen and Watt was that he, too, did not invent the steam engine. In 1663 Edward Somerset, second Marquis of Worcester, published a book detailing his many inventions, quaintly titled (for short) *A Century of the Names and Scantlings of Inventions by me already Practiced.* Among the hundred or so inventions is what Worcester called a 'water-commanding engine'; a steam-powered pump which he had patented in 1662, more than 30 years before Savery received his patent. Although no drawings for the machine remain, one was known to have been installed at Raglan Castle in Monmouth, Wales some time around 1665. The only remnants of this machine are a few scars cut into the stone walls in the room where it was housed. Another of Worcester's pumps was installed at Vauxhall in London, but no trace of it exists.

Half a century before Worcester's engine, a similar device had been developed by Salomon de Caus, an engineer and architect in the employ of Louis XIII of France. In his pamphlet de Caus describes a machine designed to raise water by steam: 'Water will, by the aid of fire, mount higher than its source'. But de Caus, too, seems to have been a bit of a late-comer in the struggle to harness steam power.

Among the lesser known visionaries who flourished during the late Italian Renaissance was Giambattista della Porta. By turns a mathematician, chemist, physicist, herbalist, gentleman of fortune and dabbler in astrology and alchemy, della Porta had nearly as prolific a mind as that of Leonardo da Vinci. Among his more notable inventions were the '*camera obscura*' and the 'magic lantern', forerunners of the camera and slide projector respectively. His first major work, published in 1558, when della Porta was only 23 years of age, was *Magiae Naturalis* or 'Natural Magic'. Although della Porta later expanded this work, and produced at least four more scientific and practical volumes, it is his 1606 book, *De Spiritali*, a work on the property of gases and lighter-than-air elements, that concerns us here. In this book della Porta describes how condensed steam can produce a vacuum capable of lifting a column of water to a considerable height. Far more advanced than some who followed in his footsteps, della Porta used two separate vessels – one for the boiler and another, which he called the 'forcing vessel', which served as a pistonless pump. It was, in essence, the same device that Savery would 'invent' nearly a century later.

What uses della Porta might have proposed for his invention will never be known; he had already been investigated by the Holy Office of the Inquisition around 1578 and had been forbidden to publish any philosophical or speculative works, although hard science was permissible. Nine years after the publication of *De Spiritali*, della Porta died at the ripe old age of 80.

Another, slightly earlier, luminary of the Renaissance who figures into our story is Leonardo da Vinci. Although da Vinci did not invent a steam pump, he did perform experiments with steam power. Among the dozens of inventions appearing in his 'codexes' (or compiled notebooks) is a steam-powered cannon. Conceived some time around 1488, the steam cannon – which da Vinci called an 'Architronito' in honour of the ancient Greek engineer Archimedes – worked more like a traditional steam engine than a pump in that it created force rather than suction, and was supposedly capable of throwing a cannon ball weighing 56 pounds (25 kg). Unlike many of da Vinci's inventions, there is at least some supporting evidence that his steam cannon may actually have been built. The results of any possible test-firings, however, have been lost to the pages of history.

Even earlier, and possibly more tantalizing because of the limited information available, is a report by the 12th century English monk and historian William of Malmesbury. In 1120 Malmesbury stated that in the great cathedral at Rheims, France there was an organ which operated by the pressure of released steam. If this report is accurate, not only is it the earliest known medieval application of steam power but it is also undoubtedly the world's first calliope.

For the true origins of the steam engine we must travel back 11 centuries prior to the time of William of Malmesbury, and 17 centuries prior to James Watt.

During the first century AD, at the great library in Alexandrian Egypt, there worked a mathematician, engineer, scientist and inventor named Hero (or Heron). In the tradition of earlier Greek scholars, Hero taught by demonstration as well as by lecturing. To this end he executed endless blueprints which he turned into working models and demonstrated to his students, eventually compiling his lectures into a series of scrolls.

Hero's works cover such topics as geometry, engines of war, winches, pneumatics, automatons, mechanics and metrics. In his book on pneumatics lurk more than 80 astounding inventions, including two distinctly different versions of the steam engine. The most famous of these was called the '*Aeolipile*' (or 'Ball of Aeolus', named for Aeolus, Greek god of the winds). Today known as 'Hero's Steam Turbine', the device is little more than a hollow sphere, mounted on an axle. At diametrically opposed points on the sphere are two 'L'-shaped spouts. The sphere is filled with water through one of the spouts and a fire built beneath it. When the water boils and produces steam, the vapour escapes through the spouts causing the sphere to whirl on its axis.

While the power from this particular steam engine may never have been harnessed, the same cannot be said for another of Hero's steam engines. The second of Hero's engines involved a water-filled boiler hidden inside an altar. When a fire was lit on the altar the water heated to boiling point and the resultant steam was used to siphon off enough water to fill a bucket which, when full, acted as a counterweight that, in turn, revolved a wooden cylinder connected to chains attached to the temple doors. As the cylinder turned, the chains wound around it, pulling open the doors. A clever and useful device, no doubt, but it never seems to have been applied to any more productive purpose than that for which it was originally designed.

If it seems improbable that the work of Hero could have influenced that of men over 1,000 years later, perhaps it is worth mentioning that Denis Papin – who, if you remember, invented his own version of the steam engine around 1690 – was a constant correspondent with the German mathematician Gottfried Leibniz, who translated Hero's work on pneumatics from ancient Greek into Latin, thus bringing it within reach of the wider scientific world.

It may have taken 17 centuries for Hero's steam-powered door-opener to be put to any more practical use than a water pump, but possibly until that time it was not an imperative. With the onset of the Industrial Revolution, however, a source of reliable, sustainable power had become a vital ingredient in human progress. He may not have invented the steam engine, but it was James Watt who adapted the power of steam into the motive force that would drive the machine age.

3

Samuel Morse & the Telegraph

The only image most people have today of the telegraph is the chattering box sometimes seen in the railway station in an old cowboy movie. Its obsolescence not withstanding, the telegraph was the most advanced form of communication in the world throughout the second half of the 19th century. In 1867 Western Union – the largest telegraph conglomerate in history – possessed 85,291 miles of telegraph lines, sent more than five million messages and made a clear profit of over $2 million. Without the invention of the telegraph, the development of the telephone (and to a lesser extent the electric light) would have been impossible.

According to popular belief, none of this would have been possible without the creative genius of American inventor Professor Samuel FB Morse. But first some background.

The word 'telegraphy' comes from the Greek and translates roughly as 'writing at a distance'. Nothing in the name suggests that it must be an electrical device, and there were certainly means of communicating messages over long distances before the harnessing of electricity. In the fourth century BC, Greek historian Diodorus Cronus wrote that King Darius I of Persia connected his far-flung provinces by means of a line of men, stationed on hilltops, who shouted the latest news to one another. This was no doubt crude, but reportedly 30 times faster than messages delivered by courier. The Romans improved on this system by using fire-towers (iron baskets filled with brushwood that could be set alight) to send warnings of invasion by night, and reflective, polished bronze mirrors to do the same by day. Similar methods were used in England as recently as the Napoleonic Wars.

As early as the 1620s the Italian mathematician, astronomer and physicist Galileo Galilei hinted in his *Dialogues* that he knew of a way of transmitting messages over several miles by means of magnetic needles – a method strikingly similar to 19th century telegraphs – but as he was already living under perpetual house arrest for having suggested that the Earth revolves around the Sun, it is hardly surprising that Galileo refused to expound on the idea. A lifetime after Galileo, Englishman Robert Hooke improved on the ancient fire-tower system by suggesting that men could transfer messages via placards bearing letters of the alphabet, which could be read at great distances with the aid of a telescope. Hooke's idea was never adopted, but it may well have been the inspiration for the 'optical telegraph' invented by Frenchman Claude Chappe.

In May 1792 the 29-year-old Chappe demonstrated his device before the Revolutionary

Government of France. Mounted on a pole were two opposing 'L'-shaped arms whose position could be adjusted by a series of ropes and pulleys. The position of the arms, like naval semaphore, indicated individual letters of the alphabet. Five years later the British improved on this type of telegraph, replacing Chappe's arms with six 'shutters' or panels that could be opened or closed in various combinations to produce a total of 64 letters, words and numbers. None of these telegraphs, ingenious as they may have been, was electrical in nature. That, of course, had to wait for electricity to be understood and harnessed.

The first step in this process had come in 1729 when Englishman Stephen Gray discovered that electricity 'flows'. In his first experiments Gray sent a charge of static electricity through 490 feet (150 m) of hemp string. Two years later he switched to steel wire and achieved a distance of 700 feet (213 m). Within two decades Gray had sent electrical charges across the mighty Thames river in London through an impressive 10,000 feet (c.3,000 m) of wire. Another of Gray's contributions was to discover that the transmitting wire must be insulated if the charge is to be maintained.

As early as 1753 an anonymous author, who signed himself 'CM', contributed an article to *Scots Magazine* in which he described a telegraph operated by a hand-cranked static generator. Indeed, such a machine was built in 1774 in Geneva, Switzerland by a man named Le Sage. Le Sage's machine required 26 wires – one for each letter of the alphabet – and a short burst of power was sent along whichever wire corresponded to the desired letter. Presumably it worked, but the distance it could cover would have been extremely limited.

The problem with making electricity useful was that it was only available in short, static bursts. It was not until 1799, when Alessandro Volta invented the storage battery, that a constant source of electricity became available. But the telegraph, as we know it, not only requires electricity but also an electromagnet. This was not invented until 1820 by French physicist André-Marie Ampère, who also devised the galvanometer – a device used for measuring electrical current with a dial and needle, much like a clock. Now inventors could make their choice – they could continue to work with the familiar static electricity or experiment with the new continuous current.

With all this technology at hand, inventors fairly crawled out of the woodwork, each bent on demonstrating their version of the electric telegraph. In 1806 one version was proposed by Ralph Wedgwood, nephew of Josiah Wedgwood the pottery manufacturer. In 1809 Samuel von Soemmering, of the Munich Academy of Science, developed another telegraph, and three years later came up with yet another in which the tips of 35 wires were submerged in test tubes of acid – each test tube corresponding with a letter or number. When a current passed through a wire it caused the acid to bubble. Even more bizarre was a system invented by Hubert Recy some time around the year 1830 which used electrical current to ignite small dishes of alcohol – each flaming pool corresponding to a letter of the alphabet. This was all very creative (and no doubt decorative), but not terribly practical.

The first functioning electrical telegraph was set up at the University of Göttingen, Germany in 1833 by Professor Karl Gauss (mathematics) and Professor Wilhelm Weber (physics). With wires running from the university observatory across the rooftops to a receiving station 1¼ miles (2 km) away, the telegraph used all the latest discoveries, including a storage battery for power, an electromagnet and a galvanometer as a receiver. Not only was their device used for scientific experimentation but it was also available for private messages. Although large, cumbersome and suffering from a severely limited range, it was unquestionably the world's first functioning telegraph.

In 1837 (the year Queen Victoria assumed the throne of Great Britain) the race for a better telegraph had taken on a life of its own. More than 60 inventors worked worldwide to make instantaneous communication practical; but the race was still being led by Germany. That year Karl August Steinheil developed a telegraph in which messages were printed out on a thin ribbon of paper – a system still used in the 1930s. Additionally, Steinheil discovered that he could eliminate one of the dual wires previously used to carry the messages if he grounded the equipment to the earth.

Close on Steinheil's heels was a physician and pharmacist from Devonshire, England named Edward Davy, a distant relation of Sir Humphry Davy, another experimenter in early electrical devices. What Davy discovered was that he could solve the problem of losing power over long distances by installing an electrical relay – a simple switch that would reconnect the circuit and boost the power of the signal. The more relays that were installed in the line the greater the distance that could be achieved. Aware of what he had, Davy quickly patented the device.

While Steinheil and Davy were tinkering with their telegraphs, William Fothergill Cooke was touring Europe after being mustered out of the British East India Company. While in Heidelberg, Germany Cooke attended a lecture on telegraphy given by a Professor GW Munke. The machine Munke displayed had been developed by Baron Pavel Schilling, a Russian nobleman, and seemed – at least to Cooke, who had never encountered a telegraph before – to be a wonder awaiting commercial exploitation. Cooke purchased a copy of Schilling's machine and headed back to England, convinced he could make it pay. After fiddling around with the thing for several months Cooke found himself confronted with the familiar problem of distance. Not to be discouraged, he requested a meeting with Michael Faraday, then the most respected man in the field of electrical experimentation and head of London's august Royal Institution.

The meeting seems to have got off on the wrong foot when Cooke, unable to concentrate on his main topic, began expounding ideas for a perpetual motion machine. Politely, Faraday excused himself with the suggestion that Cooke visit Peter Roget, compiler of *Roget's Thesaurus*. Roget, in turn, suggested Cooke visit Professor Charles Wheatstone at King's College, London. Wheatstone, a professor of experimental philosophy, was a physicist who, at this time, was working on a telegraph of his own. What Wheatstone knew, and told Cooke, was that the solution to the distance problem could be overcome by a relay, but that the relay patent was held by Edward Davy. Eventually, Wheatstone agreed to form a partnership with Cooke; Cooke would take care of the business while Wheatstone would develop the telegraph into a workable system. Within the month they had filed for a patent and Cooke attempted to approach Davy, only to find that he had fled the country due to unspecified marital problems, leaving his invention (and a pile of debts) in the hands of his father. The senior Davy sold the patent rights to the electric relay to Cooke and Wheatstone for £600, and by June 1837 the pair held the patent on a new and practical approach to telegraphy.

In the Wheatstone–Cooke version of the telegraph, electrical signals were sent to a series of five needles arrayed across the centre line of a diamond-shaped board. Painted on the board were letters of the alphabet, and the desired letter was indicated by

following the path of two needles to their intersection –
much in the same way mileage is located on a mileage
chart. The device was not only simple to read but also
simple to operate.

By early summer 1837, Cooke had convinced the
directors of the London & Birmingham Railway to
attend a demonstration of the new telegraph. Stringing
wire along 1½ miles (2.4 km) of track running between
London's Euston station and Camden Town, by 25 July
all was ready. Wheatstone manned one end of the line
and Cooke the other. The railway directors must have
been impressed with what they saw because two years
later a permanent line had been established between
Paddington Terminal and West Drayton station, 13½
miles (just over 20 km) away. By 1840 Cooke and Wheatstone's 'needle telegraph' was in use on both the London
& Birmingham and Great Western Railway lines.

No mention has yet been made of telegraphic
developments in America because, so far, England and
Europe were far ahead of the game. There were,
however, individuals in the US who were working hard
to narrow the communications gap. In 1832, at the
College of New Jersey (later to change its name to
Princeton University), newly installed Professor of
Natural Philosophy Joseph Henry had been working on
a telegraphic system for some time, setting up a fully
working prototype, powered by an electromagnet, on the
college grounds. Four years later – a scant one year before
Edward Davy – Henry had developed an electrical relay
and, shortly thereafter, the first functioning electric

motor. But Henry was dedicated to pure science rather than commerce and never sought to exploit the telegraph, although he did publish his findings in the *American Journal of Science* to mark it as his own work. In the US, at least, commercial exploitation of the telegraph would have to wait for someone else; someone like Professor Samuel FB Morse.

Morse was a well-respected professor at New York University. He did not teach physics or engineering, however, but art, and was instrumental in founding the National Academy of Design. In his private career he was regularly commissioned by numerous people in high society. During the summer of 1830 the 39-year-old Morse was junketing around Europe, painting and attending lectures on various subjects, possibly including at least one on the telegraph. Despite Morse's claims that his interest had been sparked by a casual ship-board conversation while returning home, it seems unlikely that a man with no technical knowledge could have envisioned such a mechanism without having seen one demonstrated and having had a chance to examine the equipment at close quarters. Whatever the case, by the time Morse returned to New York City his mind was aflame with the commercial possibilities of the telegraph.

By 1835 Morse had assembled his first, crude telegraph. Powered by a wooden clock mechanism and an electromagnet, the received signals were scratched out on a piece of paper in a zig-zagging motion not unlike a lie detector. Unfortunately, the greatest distance Morse could send a signal was slightly under 50 feet

(15 m). To find out where he was going wrong he consulted fellow faculty member and chemistry professor, Leonard Gale. Gale made several suggestions and recommended that Morse read Professor Joseph Henry's article in the *American Journal of Science* for a more detailed description of the latest telegraphic mechanisms. Morse did so, and what he learned was that he simply did not possess the technical skill to make the best possible machine. He did, however, continue demonstrating his prototype telegraph in public lectures.

Following one such lecture Morse was approached by a recent graduate of New York University named Alfred Vail. Shy and unassuming, Vail explained that he was interested in such devices and thought he could help Morse. Vail's father, it appeared, owned a wonderfully modern iron mill in Morristown, New Jersey and Alfred was certain he could use the facilities there to manufacture better telegraph equipment. After some negotiation, Vail agreed to make the necessary improvements to Morse's equipment – and at his own expense – but only if Morse ceded 25% of any future profits to him. Morse agreed and the two met at the Speedwell Ironworks to go over the details.

By mid-September 1837 a refined telegraph machine was starting to take shape, but the amount of work involved proved to be nightmarish. According to Vail's assistant, William Baxter: 'As we became acquainted with Morse it became evident to us that his mechanical knowledge and skill were limited, and his ideas in matters relating to construction of little value.' Until he saw the results of Vail's work, even Morse seemed to agree. Some years later, in a letter to a friend, Morse wrote: 'Up to the autumn of 1837 my telegraphic apparatus existed in so rude a form that I felt reluctance to have it seen.'

Excited by the improvements Vail was suggesting, Morse immediately filed a 'patent caveat' (a letter of intent stating that a full patent application would be forthcoming). In order to assist Vail, Morse entered into a long correspondence with Professor Joseph Henry. Henry offered numerous suggestions but was adamant that what Morse was doing was nothing new. In one letter he stated flatly that the idea 'would naturally arise in the mind of almost any person familiar with the phenomena of electricity'.

By the time Vail had finished revamping the system, very little remained of Morse's original design. The sending key had been redesigned, as had the recording mechanism and the relay mechanism. The new telegraph was not so much Morse's but Vail's. When Morse filed the full patent application, Vail, despite his work and 25% ownership in the company, went unnamed.

By 6 January 1838 Vail was ready to test the equipment. In this first attempt, at the Speedwell Ironworks, Vail and Morse achieved a clear signal at a distance of two miles.

The biggest problem with the system now was not the equipment but the code Morse had devised.

Individual words were assigned a numerical sequence, which had to be encoded at the sending end and then decoded at the receiving end. Again Vail came to the rescue. While Morse was drumming up financial support, Vail refined the code into a simple sequence of dots and dashes for individual letters. To ensure the simplest code possible, Vail visited a local printer's shop to find out which pieces of type were used most frequently. The letter 'e', the most often used letter in the English language, was assigned a single dot. 'J', which occurs only occasionally, was assigned the far more complex dot-dash-dash-dash, and so on through the alphabet. With the new code complete, and yet another new receiver to facilitate it, the telegraph was ready for a public demonstration.

While Vail was busy improving the Morse telegraph and Morse code, Morse himself had been lobbying the US Congress. His staunchest ally was Maine congressman Francis OJ 'Fog' Smith who promised to garner all the support necessary to fund commercial development of Morse's telegraph. All Smith wanted in return was a simple 25% of the company. Morse agreed, kept 60% for himself, gave a share to his friend Professor Gale and cut Vail's stake in the company from 25% to 12.5%. Thanks to such machinations, the US Government was persuaded to fork out $30,000 in development money.

There is no denying Morse needed the money to arrange a demonstration sufficiently grand to impress the Government. Throughout the winter of 1843, 144 telegraph poles were erected between the US Capitol building in Washington, DC and the Mount Clare Railway Depot in Baltimore, Maryland – a distance of more than 40 miles (64 km). On 24 May 1844 Morse manned a makeshift telegraph station in the US Supreme Court chambers of the Capitol Building while Vail waited at the opposite end in Baltimore. Public officials looked on at both ends of the line. The message Morse sent to Vail has gone down in history as the Biblical 'What hath God wrought!' The performance must have been generally satisfying; within a year America's first telegraph line was open for business between Washington and Baltimore. A short time later, Philadelphia and New York were connected.

With the success of Morse's telegraph, Vail's help and goodwill were perhaps no longer necessary and he was dispatched to manage a branch office of the company at the paltry salary of $900 per annum. It is not known whether he was ever paid any dividends on his 12.5% of the company. By 1848 Alfred Vail had had enough. In a letter to Morse he said: 'I have made up my mind to leave the Telegraph to take care of itself, since it cannot take care of me.' To his credit, Vail never once denounced Morse, either in public or private.

Morse may, or may not, have cared what happened to Vail, but Vail was not the only person who now had the measure of Professor Morse.

Despite his belief that Morse was reinventing the wheel, Professor Joseph Henry had done his best to advise and support Morse's efforts to popularize the telegraph. At least he did until the 1845 publication of a book written by Alfred Vail, which recounted a history of the development of the Morse–Vail telegraph. Henry felt that his contribution to the work had been grossly slighted. Of course, we have no way of knowing whether Vail was aware of Henry's input, or if Morse had allowed Vail to believe the improvements had come from him alone. Whatever the case, Henry was sufficiently upset that he wrote to Professor Charles Wheatstone saying: '...if he [Morse] suffers any more such publications to be made by his assistant he will array against him the science of this country and the world'.

In 1849 Morse levelled patent infringement suits against three rival telegraph companies, claiming that they had stolen his invention. Obviously, their best defence would be to show that Morse himself had stolen the telegraph. To assist in this, the companies subpoenaed Professor Henry. Henry only made his statement reluctantly, but when he did so he asserted that Morse's relay was based on information from his own 1831 article in the *American Journal of Science*. In his deposition Henry said it was his belief that Morse had not made 'a single original discovery in electricity, magnetism or electromagnetism, applicable to the invention of the telegraph. I have always considered his merit to consist in combining and applying the discoveries of others...'

In the end, although some of Morse's marginal claims were upheld, his overall claim to inventing the telegraph was struck down by the US Supreme Court. Furious, Morse lashed out at Henry, insisting he had been betrayed and claiming that the invention of the telegraph was his and his alone. Morse may have believed this bitter polemic, but almost no one else did.

4

Isaac Singer & the Sewing Machine

Most people no longer own a sewing machine, and those that do hardly give it a thought. The reason for this cavalier attitude toward this ingenious machine is that clothing is now so inexpensive that many of us consider it a disposable commodity. But life was not always thus. According to archaeological finds, mankind has been making and wearing clothing for about 20,000 years, and up until the middle of the 19th century, every stitch in every garment ever worn by anyone was laboriously sewn by hand. With the exception of feeding ourselves, making cloth and clothing was the most constant and time consuming of human activities.

With the dawn of the Industrial Revolution in the mid-18th century, cloth became less expensive thanks to automated looms; the clothing made from that cloth, however, was still hand sewn. The rich went to tailors and dress-makers, the middle class bought factory-made clothes and the vast majority of families made their own. That is to say, the women of the house made them. The impact of the sewing machine on women's lives is neatly expressed in two quotes from this period. In 1856, Louis Godey, publisher of the women's fashion magazine *Godey's Lady's Book*, wrote: 'This sewing machine is perhaps humanity's most blessed instrument', and three years later *Scientific American* said: 'It is astonishing how, in a few years, the sewing machine has made such strides in popular favor [going from] a mechanical wonder [to] a household necessity.'

If you happen to live in a home which still has one of these 'mechanical wonders', chances are it is a Singer. If asked who invented the sewing machine most people would, not without justification, say it must have been Mr Singer. But Isaac Singer did not invent the sewing machine, and never claimed to have. To find out why Singer's name is so closely linked to this machine we begin in New York State in the early 1830s.

Born in rural New York State in 1796, Walter Hunt was a devout Quaker who made a passable living inventing useful things. Over the course of a long career he invented the safety pin, the first repeating rifle, a knife sharpener, a streetcar bell, a flax spinner for making linen thread, artificial stone, a road-sweeping machine and numerous other practical and pragmatic devices. In the process he amassed a total of 26 US patents. In 1833–34 Hunt also invented a sewing machine. It was not the first such machine ever invented, but it was innovative in that it used a needle with the hole in the pointed end, was the first to use two spools of thread (one feeding from above and the other from below) and also the first machine to produce a locking stitch – all previous attempts had only made a chain stitch that could easily unravel if the thread broke. In most of its basic parts and overall design, Hunt's device was very much like a modern sewing machine.

As was true with most of his work, Hunt's goal was to make life easier for those who bought his inventions. While he knew the sewing machine would take much of the drudgery out of women's lives, he also feared it would put thousands of poor women, who often worked in garment factories for meagre wages, out of work. Hunt finally decided he could not risk throwing even a single woman out of work so he declined to patent his machine and quietly put it aside.

The next man to invent the sewing machine was Elias Howe. Born in 1819 in Massachusetts, Howe became an apprentice machinist at age 16 but lost his job during the economic 'panic' of 1837. Moving to Boston in the hope of securing employment, Howe found a job in the shop of precision instrument-maker Ari Davis, where his knowledge of intricate machinery increased tremendously – at least until illness forced him to quit work. While Howe was incapacitated, his wife began to take in sewing to help pay the bills. In an effort to relieve her workload, Howe decided to invent a machine that would sew. It is highly improbable that he was aware of Hunt's machine, and while his device incorporated many of the same features as Hunt's, there has never been any hint of foul play. The machine Howe finally came up with in 1844 was, by modern standards, clumsy and inefficient. The cloth was held vertically on a set of pins, and the needle (along with the arm that supported it) moved back and forth horizontally. This arrangement made it impossible to make a long, running seam. However, although the cloth had to be repositioned every few inches, it could still sew some 250 stitches a minute – a vast improvement over sewing by hand.

By 1846 Howe had obtained a patent on his device and began to show it to the public. In demonstrations all over the eastern United States he illustrated its effectiveness by challenging teams of five expert seamstresses to out-sew his machine. Invariably, the machine won; unfortunately, Howe did not. Almost no one seemed interested in buying a machine that could sew. This reluctance may have had something to do with its hefty $300 price tag. Still, Howe soldiered on. He sent his brother to England in an effort to market the machines, but after months of demonstrations Amasa Howe had only made one sale.

William Thomas owned a chain of corset-making factories and realized that Howe's machine would allow him to cut his labour costs while increasing production. He negotiated to buy the rights to the machine, but insisted that Elias come to England to help him make the contraption more adaptable to corset production. Howe complied, but his relationship with Thomas was not a happy one. Thomas was constantly displeased with Howe's improvements, and Howe hated Thomas' overbearing manner. By 1849 Howe was nearly penniless and moved his family back to the US in disgust. If things had been bad in England, they were even worse back home. It seems that during his two-year absence the sewing machine industry had taken off like a rocket. There were now dozens of manufacturers building, and selling, sewing machines – and nearly every one of them was using Howe's basic design. While Howe was trying to figure out what to do (and how to raise sufficient funds to sue the companies that had infringed on his patent), his wife died. While his wife's death may have had no immediate impact on the sewing machine, it gave one Isaac Singer, as well as other manufacturers, time to patent their own versions of the device.

Isaac Singer was, by any standard, a remarkable man. His varied career had begun as a teenager when he was apprenticed, first to a cabinet-maker and then to a machinist. While working with his older brother in 1839, the 28-year-old Singer had invented an excavating machine, the rights to which he sold for $2,000. With this windfall he started his own troupe of travelling Shakespearean players. Standing 6 feet 4 inches tall, and with a voice like rolling thunder, Singer must have dominated every stage he walked across. Unfortunately, the theatre did not provide the money necessary to satisfy Singer's expensive tastes. He loved fine dining, expensive clothes and expensive women – lots of them.

By 1844 Singer had given up the stage and gone back to the machine shops, because they paid better.

While working in Pittsburgh in 1848 he invented a machine for carving the wooden letters used by typesetters and printers. To promote this new invention he moved his two wives (yes, *two* wives) and half dozen offspring to Boston, Massachusetts where he installed the type cutter in the shop of Orson Phelps, a manufacturer of sewing machines for the Lerow & Blodgett Company. In casual conversation Phelps complained about how flawed the machines were; how inefficient to operate and how often they broke down. With the eye of an innovative machinist, Singer quickly made a number of suggestions for how they could be improved. Phelps told Singer to forget about his type-cutting machine and build a better sewing machine. So Singer did just that.

Singer's machine, like almost every other one on the market, used Howe's basic stitching apparatus, but Singer unquestionably made improvements – some of which, like John Bachelder's concept of turning the mechanism 90 degrees so the cloth lay on a flat bed and installing a ratcheted feed to move the cloth along under the needle, Singer had blithely incorporated into his machine. Still, other improvements, like a spring-loaded presser foot to keep the cloth flat on the bed, and replacing the hand crank with a foot treadle, Singer had devised himself.

By 1851 Singer had successfully patented the most user-friendly machine to date, had founded IM Singer & Co, and was ready to take his new act on the road; but he was also clever enough to know that he could not run the entire business himself. What he needed was a business partner. Enter the prim and proper Edward Clark, attorney; a more unlikely compatriot for the flamboyant Singer one could hardly imagine. Despite their apparent differences, the two men worked well together. While Singer carried out public demonstrations, Clark dealt with business and finance. He also came up with one of the most innovative sales tools of all time – paying on instalment plan. Even though Singer's machines were priced between \$75 and \$125, this was still far more than the average household could afford to pay all at once. With the new plan, a housewife could buy a machine for \$5 down and \$3–5 a week. It was a novel approach to sales, and this, along with Singer's homey showrooms done up to look like comfortable, middle-class parlours, quickly made IM Singer & Co an up-and-coming force in the burgeoning sewing machine market.

Just as Singer and others like him were carving out comfortable niches in the market, Elias Howe had recovered sufficiently from his wife's death to deal with the situation. His father agreed to take out a mortgage on the family farm so Elias would have the money to hire lawyers. With this security behind him, Howe levelled suit against half a dozen individuals – the most well-known and resourceful of whom was Isaac Singer.

Singer's first logical move was to try to discover if Howe, himself, had stolen anyone else's design. How he found him is unknown, but somehow Singer located Walter Hunt and convinced him to patent his own sewing machine, which had lain dormant for 17 years. Once Hunt had filed for his patent he filed suit against Howe. Suits, counter-suits and injunctions continued through 1852, '53 and into '54, but one by one every defence against Howe's suits collapsed. Hunt's patent application was disallowed and Singer's defence, along with that of manufacturers Grover & Baker and Wheeler & Wilson, crumbled in the face of Howe's patents.

Finally, by mid-1854, Elias Howe was recognized as the only legitimate holder of a patent relating to a sewing machine that used a needle with a hole in the point or which created a two-thread lock stitch. The defendants in the case were ordered to pay Howe $15,000 damages for patent infringement and a future royalty of $5 on every machine they sold in the US, and $1 on every machine sold abroad.

To protect themselves from this happening again in future, Singer, Grover & Baker and Wheeler & Wilson formed a consortium in 1856, pooling their patents and giving each other free access to any advancements and developments which any of them might come up with. That same year IM Singer manufactured 2,564 machines, and four years later, in 1860 (with the US Government buying machines by the hundreds to manufacture military uniforms for the imminent Civil War), he made some 13,000 machines. Other manufacturers, including Elias Howe (who had gone back into business in Bridgeport, Connecticut), also prospered.

So if Isaac Singer did not invent the sewing machine, who did? As mentioned at the beginning of the chapter, Walter Hunt invented a sewing machine, but as we also mentioned, it was not the first. The first known device to automatically run a seam was patented in 1755 by a German named Charles Wiesenthal, who had emigrated to England. Wiesenthal's machine (British patent number 701) had certain limitations. The entire needle, along with a length of thread, passed entirely through the fabric. This meant that only a short length of thread could be used and a new piece of thread had to be inserted after every few inches of seam. Unfortunately, only the design for the needle remains, and whether or not he actually invented the entire machine (or only the needle) is lost in the mists of time.

Thirty-five years later, in 1790, London cabinet-maker Thomas Saint submitted a patent for, as he described it in his patent application, 'An Entire New Method of Making and Completing Shoes, Boots, Splatterdashes, Clogs and Other Articles, by Means of Tools and Machines also Invented by Me for that Purpose'. The patent application actually covers three entirely different machines, one of which was intended to sew cloth. The machines were cumbersome and awkward to use, but the one designed to sew fabric contained many features still found on modern sewing machines, including a horizontal table on which the cloth was laid, an overhead arm holding the needle and a continuous thread fed into the machine from a spool.

Saint's machine could only produce a chain stitch, but it was the first fully developed sewing machine ever patented. Unfortunately, because there was no appropriate place in the British Patent Office to file such a piece of equipment, it was stashed away among new formulas for glue and laid undiscovered until 1873.

It is not known whether Saint ever tried to manufacture his machine, but when the patent was eventually discovered, and a model made from his plans, it required significant re-working before it would run a single stitch. Possibly Saint found this out for himself and gave up on the whole idea.

Around 1800 one Baltasar Krembs from Mayan, Germany invented a machine designed to sew caps, and while his machine (like those of Hunt and Howe) featured a needle with a hole at the pointed end, there is no record that he ever patented, or built, the thing. Almost simultaneous with Krembs, the team of Thomas Stone and James Henderson patented a design for a sewing machine, as did Scotsman John Duncan. Duncan's machine was specifically designed for embroidery and featured multiple needles, but it, like those of Stone and Henderson, and Krembs, never seems to have made it beyond the planning stage.

The first known, apparently successful, sewing machine was probably designed in 1814 by Josef Madersperger, an Austrian tailor. Madersperger's machine utilized a double pointed needle and was designed specifically to sew clothes with a simple chain stitch, rather than the lock stitch we know today.

Although Madersperger lacked the funds to build and market his machine, he designed an improved model in 1830 – but it, like its predecessor, seems never to have developed beyond a single working model. The first sewing machine patents in the US were handed out to John Adams Doge of Vermont and Henry Lye of Philadelphia in 1818 and 1826 respectively. Doge's machine seems to have been nearly as labour intensive as hand sewing and Lye's patent application and drawings were so badly damaged in a fire at the Patent Office that the efficacy of the machine cannot be determined by studying the charred remnants. However effective or ineffective it may have been, there is no record that Lye attempted to market his invention.

If commercial success, along with good engineering, is the hallmark of true invention then the real inventor of the sewing machine is most probably Parisian tailor Barthélemy Thimonnier. In 1830 – just three years prior to Hunt's sewing machine – Thimonnier patented a practical, functional sewing machine. Being an enterprising sort, Thimonnier convinced the French Government of the practicality of his machine in producing vast numbers of military uniforms. By 1841 Thimonnier had installed 80 of the machines in his factory and was churning out uniforms like sausages. Unfortunately, his fellow tailors seem to have been a volatile bunch who took exception to this new-fangled approach to putting tailors and seamstresses out of work. One night a mob broke into Thimonnier's factory and destroyed the machines before setting the place alight and heading off to confront the man himself. With the mob hard on his heels, Thimonnier managed to escape to England with one of his precious machines, but his star had faded. Although his sewing machine was awarded a First Class Medal at the Paris World Fair of 1855, it was too little and too late to be of any use to Thimonnier, who was by then ekeing out the last 18 months of life in an English poorhouse.

Fortunately, this story has a rather happier ending for both Elias Howe and Isaac Singer. When the American Civil War broke out in 1861, Howe spent some of his new-found fortune equipping the entire 17th Connecticut Volunteer Regiment – presumably with uniforms run up on Howe machines. Howe himself joined the regiment as a simple private and served throughout the war. Although he died in 1867, two years after the war's end (at the relatively young age of 48), Howe left behind an estate worth more than $2 million.

Around the time of Howe's death his old nemesis, Isaac Singer, retired from the sewing machine business and moved abroad with the latest in his string of (often overlapping) 'wives' and at least some of the 24 children he acknowledged fathering. After a stint in France – which he was forced to flee during the Franco–Prussian War – he settled in the town of Torquay in the south west of England. There, as befitted his ever-modest tastes, he bought an estate complete with a 115-room house and a coach house with ample space for his 50 carriages. When Singer passed away at the age of 63 in 1875 he left behind an estate worth something in excess of $14 million along with 18 surviving children and numerous wives, ex-wives and mistresses who spent the remainder of their own lives squabbling over who got how much of the money. Do you suppose any of them ever paused, even once, to wonder who had really invented the machine that had made them all so rich?

5

Charles Darwin & the Theory of Evolution

Of all the individuals discussed in this book, Charles Darwin is probably the only one whose name can still spark heated discussion. Some 150 years after the publication of his books, *On The Origin of Species by Means of Natural Selection* (commonly known as '*The Origin of Species*') and *The Descent of Man, and Selection in Relation to Sex* ('*The Descent of Man*'), many people still fail (or refuse) to grasp what he was saying.

However, before going any further, let us establish exactly what the Theory of Evolution is. First, the word 'evolution' simply means a slow process of change which takes place over a long period of time. For example, almost no one would argue that modern people aren't, on average, taller than our ancestors of six or eight generations ago. This is one example of evolution. Secondly, evolution is not a theory. It is a fact in just the same way as Isaac Newton's Gravitational Theory and Albert Einstein's Theory of Relativity or his Unified Field Theory are facts. The only part of the Theory of Evolution that remains theoretical is precisely how, and why, the evolutionary process takes place.

The idea that life forms change, or evolve, over time certainly did not originate with Darwin or any of his contemporaries. More than two millennia ago Greek philosophers Anaximander (*c.*600 BC) and Epicurus (*c.*300 BC) postulated that animals must adapt to changing environments or they would die. The way they phrased this hypothesis may not have been scientific, but the idea of life adapting and changing was certainly there.

While similar theories may have been postulated over the centuries, the first person to formalize them into recognizable scientific thought was Baron Georges Léopold Chrétien Frédéric Dagobert Cuvier (1769–1832), whom we will refer to simply as Cuvier. Like most men of the 18th and 19th centuries who studied nature, Cuvier was referred to as a 'naturalist'. Unlike most naturalists, however, Cuvier was a zoologist and a trained anatomist, and was instrumental in establishing the field of paleontology. In 1795, at the age of 26, Cuvier had already secured a job as assistant to the Professor of Comparative Anatomy at the National Museum of Natural History in Paris. Taking his job as seriously as he had taken his studies at university, within a few years Cuvier had established a reputation as one of the world's leading experts on animal anatomy.

Integral to the museum's collection was a vast and constantly growing collection of fossils. By the close of the 18th century, fossils were nothing new; they had been around for millions of years (naturally) and people had been collecting and displaying them for nearly a century. But Cuvier looked at them in a slightly different way; what he did, that no one had done before, was compare the creatures embedded in stone with their cousins who still walked the Earth. When elephant-like fossils were found in Europe and North America, most zoologists accepted the fact that, although elephants may no longer live in the Northern Hemisphere, there were still plenty of them wandering around in Africa and India. Elephant habitat may have changed, but elephants – like all plant and animal life – remained constant, just as it had been set out at the Creation as described in the Book of Genesis. Alternatives to such orthodoxy were unacceptable. It was widely accepted that God had designated how many and what kinds of plants, animals and insects there would be at the dawn of time, and this number must remain constant if the 'Great Chain of Life' was to remain intact. Cuvier saw things a little differently.

In his first scientific paper, entitled '*Mémoires sur les Espèces d'éléphants Vivants et Fossiles*', published in 1800, Cuvier stated flatly that the elephant-like fossils were, in fact, not at all like modern-day elephants. The conclusion was simple; somehow, at some point in the distant past, this particular type of elephant (it was actually a mammoth) had ceased to exist. At the end of his article, Cuvier wrote: 'All of these facts, consistent among themselves... seem to me to prove the existence of a world previous to ours, destroyed by some kind of catastrophe.'

As obvious as this may seem to most of us today, Cuvier's paper was nothing less than scandalous. If, as Cuvier proposed, life forms could simply wink in and out of existence, then the world as we knew it was not the world as it was laid down by God at the Creation. If this were true, then there were only two possibilities: 1) the Chain of Life was breaking down and God's universe was falling apart, or 2) life on Earth had never been stable and was in a constant state of change and flux. In either case the implications for our own existence and state of being, as well as God's ability to control the universe, were too terrible to contemplate. Inevitably, this heretical concept began to spread.

Jean-Baptiste Pierre Antoine de Monet, the Chevalier de Lamarck, was 25 years older than Cuvier but, lacking Cuvier's early good fortune, did not develop his own theories on life in the past until almost the same time as the younger man.

After studying fossil collections throughout France and Western Europe, Lamarck agreed with Cuvier that some types of animals and plants had ceased to exist, but close comparison of fossilized remains and the bone structure of modern animals led him to hypothesize that not only did some life forms disappear, but that others changed; probably in order to adapt to a changing environment. The concept was so radical that even Lamarck could not accept it without providing an underlying reason why God would allow such things to happen. He postulated that evolution was, in fact, an innate, unconscious striving toward perfection. In an article published in 1801 – the year after Cuvier's paper appeared – Lamarck stated that when conditions were right, organisms would slowly evolve into higher organisms. The ultimate goal, presumably, was for each living thing to become as much like humanity as possible. To fill the gaps thus created at the lowest end of the biological social ladder, simple forms of life were created spontaneously. Lamarck envisioned a two-tiered evolutionary process. There were quick evolutionary advancements, where a developed characteristic (such as athletic ability) of a parent could be passed on to an offspring but not necessarily to an entire species. Additionally, he stated that if a species did not use an organ or body part for a long enough time it would simply wither away and disappear.

While the results of Lamarck's version of evolution would have been indistinguishable from the process as we now understand it, the methodology was in error. But given that no scientific groundwork existed on which to build his concepts, Lamarck's theories were impressively close to the truth.

Within a matter of months the concept of extinction (and its handmaid, evolution) had both come into existence; a wave of scientific and theological backlash was inevitable. Lamarck in particular bore the brunt of almost everyone's anger, including that of Cuvier, who could not accept evolution because he did not see extinction as part of a slow, continual process but only as something that came about through cataclysmic change, such as the Great Flood of Genesis.

Eight years after Cuvier and Lamarck first pushed the heresy of evolution into the light of day, Robert and Susannah Darwin's fifth child was born. Scientific inquiry had always loomed large in the Darwin family. Robert Darwin was a society physician interested in the latest techniques and practices in medicine, and his father, Erasmus Darwin, had helped conduct investigations into the nature of marine life which proved that all animals, from humans to the humblest bivalves, had similar organs and therefore were all inter-related – a radical theory for its day. His mother was also from a high-achieving family, her father being pottery magnate Josiah Wedgwood.

No doubt Robert Darwin expected his son Charles to enter the medical profession and, at the age of 16, duly enrolled him in Edinburgh's prestigious medical school. Belatedly realizing that Charles had more interest in the natural world than in human illness, Charles' education was shifted in 1827 to Cambridge, with a major in theology. This was not an unnatural choice for a young man interested in becoming a naturalist; most noted naturalists and zoologists in Britain were members of the clergy and the Church still held a lock on scientific orthodoxy. Charles applied himself only enough to get by, clearly yearning for something more exciting than stuffy classrooms.

In the summer of 1831 one of his professors offered him the chance to join an expedition to South America and the Pacific Islands that was seeking someone willing to serve as the expedition's naturalist.

The position was unpaid, but Darwin leaped at the chance. While packing his things for the proposed two-year trip, Darwin's professor gave him a book to take along. Entitled *Principles of Geology*, and written by a man named Charles Lyell, Darwin was told that Lyell's theories – that the Earth's surface had evolved and changed gradually over millions of years, rather than being formed by a few, cataclysmic upheavals at the dawn of time – were interesting but by and large preposterous and not to be taken seriously. What Darwin would see during the voyage proved to him that Lyell was right and popular orthodoxy was wrong.

As the HMS *Beagle* plied her way down the east coast of South America, up the west and into the Pacific, Darwin took every opportunity to go ashore and study whatever animals, plants or natural phenomena he could find. In the Andes, at a height of 12,000 feet (approximately 3,600 metres), he found fossils of long-extinct marine life. How did they get there, and what happened to make the creatures disappear? At one point he was caught in an earthquake and watched the land rise and fall around him. In Argentina he saw an ostrich-like bird, known as a rheas, that was obviously related to a smaller bird living far to the south in Patagonia. What was the exact nature of their relationship, and were they related to the actual ostrich which lived in Africa? In the Galapagos Islands he saw cormorants that had lost the ability to fly and iguanas that had gained the ability to swim. Why were these isolated groups of animals different from their cousins elsewhere?

Tying all his observations together, Darwin came to the inescapable conclusion that life on Earth changed both as a result of slow, natural development and also as a result of catastrophic events. He slowly realized that those animals best able to adapt to their environment were more likely to survive than their less prepared neighbours, be they of the same species or a different species altogether. Darwin worked his findings and hypothesis into a series of papers that he regularly sent back to England, where they were read at the Cambridge Philosophical Society and then at the Geological Society in London. By the time the *Beagle* returned, the proposed two-year voyage had stretched into five, and Darwin's series of well-thought-out papers had made him a celebrity in liberal-minded scientific circles. In 1836, the year of his return, he was made a fellow of the Geological Society, and three years later elected to London's Royal Society.

As Darwin pondered what he had seen on his journey he also continued to collect any and all information he could find against which he could test his theories and hypothesis. He contacted animal breeders, plant breeders, naturalists, zoologists and geologists, gratefully accepting any useful information they might be willing to offer. Eventually he began to understand the mechanism by which animals adapted to their surroundings. Birds with a longer beak might be more likely to get the best grubs and animals with longer necks might be able to reach higher into the trees. As these useful traits were passed on from generation to generation the physical appearance of the animals themselves would also change. According to Darwin's calculations, these more favourable traits would, indeed, be passed on because the less well adapted members of a species would slowly die out. The name for this weeding-out process – 'natural selection'.

Darwin was smart enough to realize that what he was proposing – that the natural world was in an almost constant state of flux and that animals were not already perfectly adapted to their environment – might be deeply disturbing to many people. In his notebooks he even alluded to the way early scientists such as Galileo had been persecuted for revealing their discoveries. As a result, Darwin kept his findings secret from all but a few trusted colleagues – which now included Charles Lyell, author of *Principles of Geology* – and vowed to keep quiet, at least until he had answers to every possible objection that anyone might make to his theories. For the next 20 years Darwin would check his facts, develop his theory and check again.

Darwin had been refining his ideas for a decade when a young man named Alfred Russel Wallace, and his friend Henry Bates, set out on a specimen-gathering expedition to the Amazon basin.

Wallace had already worked his way through a variety of careers including map-maker, architect, agricultural chemist and teacher of English, arithmetic and drafting – and done it all before his 25th birthday. In his spare time he developed an interest in naturalist pursuits and read such popular works on the subject as

Lyell's *Principles of Geology*. It was in 1844, while teaching drafting and mathematics at Leicester, that he met Henry Bates (who had something of a reputation as a collector of beetles, then a national fad) and discovered that they had many interests in common, including a fascination with nature. Together the two men decided they would undertake a trip up the largely unexplored Amazon river and finance their adventure by collecting, and selling, samples of whatever plants, animals, fossils and insects they found along the way. The pair landed in Brazil in May 1848, and although they parted ways at some point over the next 18 months, they both continued to explore; Bates moving southward and Wallace carrying on up the Amazon.

For years Wallace continued to travel, explore, collect and write about his findings. By 1854 he had worked his way through much of Brazil and moved on to Malaysia. The following year he published a ground-breaking paper on how different species of birds and animals are distributed across different land masses. Printed in *Annals and Magazine of Natural History*, and entitled 'On the Law which has Regulated the Introduction of New Species', the paper dealt with how topography either assisted, or hindered, the range of different species of animals. At the end of the paper, Wallace concluded that 'every species has come into existence coincidental in both space and time with a closely allied species'.

Such a statement may now seem both obvious and tepid, but in 1855 it was fairly radical stuff.

By early 1856 Darwin's friend Charles Lyell had read Wallace's article and immediately passed it on to Darwin with a rather frantic note. Darwin seems to have taken Wallace's piece at face value, and not felt it to be any threat to his own long-gestating work. In fact, in May 1857, Darwin wrote to Wallace congratulating him on the piece, noting 'similar conclusions' between their theories and admitting that he had already been working on his idea for 20 years and was still two years or more from going to press.

Thirteen months later, in June 1858, Darwin may have been more than a little surprised when he received a 20-page paper from Wallace called 'On the Tendency of Varieties to Depart Indefinitely from the Original Type' in which he described his theories on the evolutionary process. His theories were almost a carbon copy of Darwin's ideas, but Wallace had clearly explained in a scant 20 pages what Darwin had needed thousands of pages to say. Immediately, Darwin wrote back to Wallace and contacted Lyell. To Wallace, he expressed his admiration for the work and offered to send the piece 'to any journal' where Wallace might want to see it published. From Lyell he sought advice, adding ruefully 'he could not have made a better short abstract [of my work]... all my originality, whatever it may amount to, will be smashed'.

Sagely, Lyell, in concert with the respected botanist Joseph Hooker, suggested that both Wallace's paper, and one which Darwin should write up immediately, should be delivered at the same meeting of London's prestigious Linnean Society. Darwin accepted the compromise and wrote a letter to Wallace telling him about the joint reading of their papers and expressing his hope that Wallace would not be offended. Just how rushed the whole thing was is evidenced by the fact that Darwin and Wallace's papers were only added to the agenda on 30 June, the meeting itself being scheduled for the next day.

The following January Darwin received an answer from Wallace. He said that he would have been very sad if his own work had been published before Darwin's and that he was glad if he had helped move Darwin closer to publication. It was all very gentlemanly and above board and no acrimony ever seems to have developed between Wallace and Darwin over first publication. As it was, Darwin set to work revising, editing and shortening the work. With the revised title of *On The Origin of Species by Means of Natural Selection, or The Preservation of Favoured Races in the Struggle for Life*, the now shortened manuscript was submitted to publisher John Murray, who had intended to publish only 500 copies but revised the first print run upward to 1,250 due to the publicity Darwin had been receiving. When the book came out in November 1859 the entire first run had already sold out in pre-order. Over the next dozen years it would go through a total of six printings.

In a copy of *The Origin of Species* that he sent to Wallace, Darwin inscribed the words: 'God knows what the public will think.' Amazingly, nearly everyone seemed to approve of the book's science, if not its theological implications. If you, dear reader, were expecting more controversy, bear in mind that this work dealt with a wide variety of species and how they have adapted, or failed to adapt, to their surroundings over extended periods of time.

Some time after the joint presentation of their papers at the Linnean Society, Wallace wrote to Darwin and asked him if he would be dealing with human origins in his book. Darwin replied: 'I think I shall avoid the whole subject...' Eventually, both men would deal with this ultimately sticky topic, and while it is Charles Darwin who has taken all the flak, abuse and fall-out, it was actually Wallace who published the theories first.

In 1864, long before Darwin took any public stand on the origins of humanity and their relationship with lower animals, Alfred Wallace produced a paper entitled 'The Origin of Human Races and the Antiquity of Man Deduced from the Theory of Natural Selection'. On reading the paper, Darwin admitted that Wallace's work was far too insightful to be ignored or overlooked, and Wallace is cited more often than any other source in Darwin's 1871 book on the same subject; *The Descent of Man*.

All things considered, Darwin may ultimately have wished he had left the field to Wallace and steered clear of the minefield of human evolution. Although Wallace never gained the fame of Darwin, neither did he suffer the vilification and humiliation that was heaped on the 'monkey man'. While most scientists in Great Britain and on the Continent gave guarded approval to

Darwin's writings, the clergy, the public and America's scientists were scandalized that anyone could suggest that it was, as so aptly stated by naturalist Thomas Huxley, 'as respectable to be a modified monkey as it is to be modified dirt'.

In all, Darwin wrote a total of four books on the joint themes of natural selection and evolution; these were virtually his entire life's work. Alfred Russel Wallace, on the other hand, went on to write a total of 150 pieces, including books, essays, articles and monographs, the majority of which focused on some aspect of natural selection and how geography determines the distribution of animal life across the globe. Still, it will always be Charles Darwin, the sad-faced old man with the Santa Claus beard, who is pilloried for having suggested that human beings were descended from apes which, just to set the record straight, he never did. What Darwin said was that human beings and the great apes (including gorillas and chimpanzees) were descended from a common ancestor.

An intriguing question remains; had it not been for Alfred Russel Wallace and his 1858 paper, would Darwin have ever gotten around to publishing *The Origin of Species*? Because Darwin flatly stated to Wallace in a letter of 1858 that he did not intend tackling the subject of human evolution, was it Wallace's 1864 piece that finally convinced him to enter the fray? Whatever the case, without the work of both Darwin *and* Wallace the scientific investigation into human origins, and the origins of the natural world, might have been stalled for decades.

6

Thomas Crapper & the Flushing Toilet

On rare occasions when conversation lags and trivia takes over, the name of Thomas Crapper often crops up. Someone will volunteer that he invented the flushing toilet, someone else will say that he was 'Sir' Thomas Crapper, and most of the group will insist he is fictitious. The truth of the matter is that there was a real Thomas Crapper, and he did manufacture plumbing goods. However, he was never knighted, and he was not the inventor of the flushing toilet.

The confusion as to who Crapper was, and what he did, came about as a consequence of a 1969 tongue-in-cheek biography of the man entitled *Flushed with Pride*. There is also Crapper's name, which appears to be the victim of what scholars call 'nominative determinism' – where a person's name determines what they become in life. Certainly the term 'crap', meaning the chaff from cereal grain in the UK, and offal or excrement in the US, existed before Thomas Crapper's time. It is possible that the rude American slang term for the toilet, the 'crapper', came about when American soldiers first saw our man's name imprinted on toilets during World War

I. So much for what Crapper was *not*; but what, and who, was he, and why is he forever connected with the porcelain throne?

Born in 1836, at the age of 14 Crapper became an apprentice to a London plumber. Some years later, in 1861, he went into partnership with Robert Wharam to establish the firm of Thomas Crapper & Co. A tremendous self-publicist and promoter, Crapper opened one of the world's first plumbing fixture showrooms, where he proudly displayed items like toilets and bath tubs; something no proper Victorian businessman would ever have dared do. Crapper's boldness, however, paid off. When Britain's royal family decided to remodel their country estate at Sandringham in the 1880s, it was to Crapper they turned for the updating of the royal bathrooms – all 30 of them. Playing up his appointment as Royal Sanitary Engineer, Crapper continued the publicity campaign that kept him at the forefront of the plumbing fixture trade for more than a decade.

The products with which Crapper became most intimately connected were a series of improved toilet designs, including the now nostalgic water closet (WC) with its reservoir mounted high on the wall. Advertised as 'Crapper's Valveless Water Waste Preventer (Patent # 4990) – One moveable part only', it was this highly efficient toilet that ensured Crapper's financial and historical success.

Thomas Crapper did indeed invent, and patent, a number of plumbing devices; nine to be precise. Four were improved drains, one a pipe joint, one a manhole cover and three were for improvements on toilets, including a device called a 'floating ballcock' which reduced leakage, and a clever foot-pedal flushing device. None of these included the widely advertised patent number 4990. That item, it seems, was invented by one Albert Giblin. We have no reason to believe that Mr Crapper stole the idea, or the patent, from Mr Giblin since he openly displayed the patent number on his product. Had there been any illegality involved, Crapper would have been advertising his own guilt. We must assume then that, recognizing a good thing when he saw it, Crapper simply bought the patent rights from Giblin.

Another device nearly as close to Crapper's heart as the valveless water waste preventer was the 'syphonic flushing device'; essentially a vacuum pump that allowed the wall-mounted cistern to refill automatically once it had emptied. The syphonic flush was a vast improvement on earlier ways of refilling the tank, but during Crapper's hey-day – the 1880s and '90s – syphonic flushing devices were being patented at the rate of 20 per year, and none of them was patented by Crapper. Again, Thomas Crapper was just a canny businessman who promoted his product to the hilt and was smart enough to realize that all his hopes lay in waste.

Amusing as all this may seem, waste disposal is a serious matter and, until relatively recent times, a seemingly insoluble problem. According to the World

Health Organization, even today nearly 40% of the world's population has no access to sanitary waste disposal facilities. Two centuries ago that figure was closer to 100%.

So long as the human population remained tiny (and people lived in small groups), waste disposal was not a matter of concern; move downstream a few paces to take care of personal business and the village remained clean. But that was a very long time ago. Even as early as Old Testament times, the matter of sewage disposal was so acute that hygienic admonishments figured in Sacred Writ. In Deuteronomy, Chapter 23, we read: 'Thou shalt have a place also without the camp, whither thou shalt go forth abroad... thou shalt dig there and shall turn back and cover that which comes from thee.'

Once cities developed, the problem became infinitely more complex – and pressing. Virtually every city dweller in the ancient and classical world used chamber pots similar to those still in use in the mid-19th century and, as was still common a few centuries ago, simply threw their contents out of the window onto the street below. Greek dramatist Aeschylus wryly referred to this hail of dross as 'missiles of mirth', but there was little mirth for those wading through it. The Romans enacted what they called the 'Dejecti Effusive Act', a prohibition against flinging the contents of portable toilets from open windows. However, recognizing that the waste had to go somewhere, the law only applied during daylight hours.

Over 1,500 years later, England's King Richard II (reigned 1377–1399) was plagued with the same intractable problem and attempted to solve it by passing the '*Statuto Quo Nul Ject Dung*' – 'The Statute Prohibiting the Dumping of Dung'. We can assume that the law had about as much effect in Richard's time as it had in ancient Rome.

In an attempt to contain the noxious smells permeating his rarefied Whitehall Palace, Henry VIII constructed a massive privy that included two long rows of toilets, set back to back, on two floors of one wing of the palace. Called the 'Great House of Easement', it was for the use of courtiers during official breaks from state business; presumably the facilities on one floor were for men and the other for ladies. A fine effort, but the effluence, along with the contents of His Majesty's royal chamber pot (covered in black velvet and studded with 2,200 golden upholstery nails), was simply dumped into the Thames to add to the pollution. For those outside the royal residence the solution remained the same as it always had; open the shutters, cry '*Gardez l'eau!*' ('Watch out for the water!') and heave it onto the pavement. While this quaint custom only added to the filth, it did give the English the word 'loo', still a slang term for toilet (itself derived from the French '*toilette*', one's personal ablutions and grooming).

So who really did invent the flushing toilet? The earliest design for a modern toilet seems to have been made by none other than that man of embarrassing brilliance, Leonardo da Vinci. During his final exile in

France, during the early years of the 16th century, da Vinci designed a water-fed toilet system for the palace of his host, King Francis (François) I. Unfortunately, like so many of his inventions, it seems never to have been constructed. Possibly Francis was happy to play out his cards without the advantage of a royal flush!

For the first European evidence of a working toilet we have to move back to England and forward in time about 80 years.

Sir John Harington was a courtier, writer, poet and one of Queen Elizabeth I's 102 godchildren. He was also blessed with an acerbic wit and a sharp tongue. In and out of favour at court, Harington was often forced to retire to his country estate at Kelston where, in 1596, he wiled away his idle hours by inventing the first functioning toilet in Europe. Operating on a system similar to that still used in modern airplane toilets, it had a closing valve at the bottom of the bowl and a water-fed cistern above. To immortalize his achievement, Harington penned a lengthy bit of doggerel entitled *A New Discourse of a Stale Subject, Called the Metamorphosis of Ajax*. 'Ajax' being a play on the term 'jakes', then already a common English slang term for the potty.

While many at court found the poem rude beyond belief, the Queen was both amused (despite the book's bawdy allusions to her favourite, the Earl of Leicester) and fascinated, and travelled to Harington's home to see the contraption for herself. Being so personally fastidious that she insisted on taking a bath once a month 'whether she needed it or not', Elizabeth dubbed the device a marvel of hygiene, returned Harington to court and demanded he install one at the palace. In gratitude, Harington penned another piece called *Plan Plots of a Privy of Perfection*; the Queen was so pleased that she had a copy bound in fine leather and hung on the bath-room wall next to the Ajax. Unfortunately, when Elizabeth passed away in 1603, so did the Ajax; it would be more than 150 years before Harington's toilet was reinvented.

Alexander Cumming was born in Edinburgh but moved to London in his youth to pursue a varied career as mathematician, mechanic and watch-maker. While making a living as a watch-maker, Cumming was successful enough in his more scientific endeavours to be elected a fellow of the Royal Society. In 1775 he also took out the first British patent for a flushing toilet. The device was similar to Harington's in that it had a sliding plate which remained closed, except during flushing, when it opened long enough to allow the waste to wash away. Innovative in Cumming's design was the use of swirling water to help clear the waste and an 'S'-shaped trap beneath the bowl. This trap filled with water after each use, preventing sewer gas from escaping into the room. This first mechanical toilet began to enjoy some success, but it was only functional for those few buildings which had their own water supply.

Only three years later, in 1778, a 30-year-old cabinet-maker, locksmith and mechanical engineer named Joseph Bramah improved on Cumming's design. He retained the 'S' trap but replaced the sliding valve at the bottom of the bowl with a hinged valve and installed a second valve in the cistern to control the amount of water used during flushing. When the handle was pulled down, the cistern emptied into the bowl, removing the waste; when it was returned (by hand) to the original position, it allowed a 15-second delay so the bowl would refill before the water shut off. In design the copper bowl looked a bit like a medieval whisky still (and like all previous models it was rather leaky and smelly), but it was definitely on the way to becoming a modern toilet.

The next improvement in toilet science would not arrive for three quarters of a century, and by then London had become a very toxic place indeed.

Having set up in the plumbing business in 1838, George Jennings had always been interested in making a better toilet, but it was not until the middle of the century that his ideas came to fruition. For years Jennings had tested various toilet designs. When trying out a new model he routinely tossed 10 small apples, a chunk of sponge and four pieces of crumpled paper into the bowl and pulled the handle. If everything cleared, Jennings declared the mechanism successful. His greatest contribution to the toilet was to make it available to a large number of people. In 1851 he installed public toilets in the newly constructed Crystal Palace, built for the Great Exhibition. Known politely as 'retiring rooms' (and commonly as 'monkey closets'), during the Exhibition's run more than 800,000 people paid good money to experience their first moment on a real toilet. The problem was that London was now home to more than two million people and still had no sewage treatment system. Everything, be it chamber pot, outhouse or Jennings toilet, emptied into the Thames, just as it had more than 1,000 years earlier.

Three years prior to the opening of the Great Exhibition, England had been hit by what can only be described as a public health crisis of near Biblical proportions. Largely due to open sewers and polluted rivers seeping their poison into the water table, in 1848 an outbreak of cholera claimed the lives of 14,000 people in London and another 40,000 across the rest of the country. Frantically, Parliament tried to deal with the situation by passing the first Public Health Act, which made it mandatory for all new buildings to have improved sanitary facilities. Another £5 million was doled out for sanitary research and, at long last, the construction of a functioning public sewer system was begun. Still, these things do not happen overnight.

The summer of 1858 – precisely a decade after the cholera epidemic – was particularly hot and dry. The level of the Thames dropped and millions of tons of rotting human waste were exposed to the air. The 'Great Stink' was so intolerable that when Parliament met to debate what was to be done they covered the windows with curtains soaked in chloride of lime to combat the stench. Nothing helped, and thousands fled the reek of London, terrified of another outbreak of plague.

An immediate attempt was made to deal with the worst of the situation by supplying safe, effective sanitary ware to those tens of thousands of homes and buildings not yet equipped with running water and sewers. The 'earth closet' was a dirt-filled, indoor privy in which ash or granulated clay was dispensed over the waste material. Essentially an early composting toilet, it was a help, but the closet was neither a toilet as we know it nor was it a solution.

As more and more sections of the metropolis were connected to the new sewer lines, the demand for flushing toilets rose dramatically, and by the century's three-quarter mark the market for modern plumbing could not have been better. Thomas Crapper & Co had already joined the stampede to cash in on the situation, but Crapper was far from alone in exploiting this marketing bonanza. In 1876 pottery manufacturer Thomas Twyford began selling the first porcelain toilets, and seven years later (in 1883) he marketed the first one-piece toilet – where the tank sat directly on the bowl – that featured an improved 'P' rather than the previous 'S'-shaped trap. Known as the 'Unitas', Twyford's toilet was relatively inexpensive, did not leak and did not smell. According to Twyford's advertising, it was 'the perfection of cleanliness'. Also revolutionary to the Unitas was a lifting wooden seat that could be raised for the convenience of gentlemen.

By the mid-1880s the toilet had evolved into something entirely recognizable to every modern user, and it had only taken it nearly 400 years and the invention of a functional sewer system to get there.

Naturally, this is not quite the end of the story or, rather, not its beginning. Notice that we referred to Harington's toilet as 'the first functioning toilet in Europe'. Though many of us like to believe the contrary, Europe – and by extension Great Britain and the Americas – is not the entire world. In July 2006 Reuter's News Agency released an article in which Chinese archaeologists stated that they had unearthed an ancient imperial tomb fitted with a water-fed toilet. Dating from the Han Dynasty (206 BC–220 AD), this would predate da Vinci's unbuilt design by a cool 1,600 years. This is all very impressive – and undoubtedly convenient for the spirits forced to spend eternity in the sealed tomb – but it is still not a winner.

For reasons unknown, the period around the second millennium BC seems to have been a watershed for toilet development. Around 1700 BC the great palace of King Minos at Knossos, on the Greek island of Crete, was fitted with a flushing toilet. Having a water-holding reservoir and a wooden seat it qualified, in all respects, as a modern toilet. It would probably have irked Minos if he had known it, but King Sargon (known as 'Sargon the Great') had an almost identical potty, but he had ruled Akkad between 2340 and 2284 BC, and thereby had his toilet about 500 years before Minos. If you are thinking that kings get everything first, consider the Harappan people who lived in what is now Pakistan and north-western India. As early as 2500 BC toilets supplied with a constantly running supply of water were featured in the vast majority of houses and the waste was carried away in a covered drainage system. So why did it take the rest of us over 4,000 years to catch up?

Before we end this tale we need to tidy up a bit of paperwork. We now know where the toilet originated, but who invented toilet paper?

The first recorded manufacture of toilet paper comes from the Chinese Bureau of Imperial Supplies. The records first mention this unmentionable in the year 1391 when 720,000 sheets were produced. Why they measured 2 feet by 3 feet (0.6 m x 0.9 m) remains unclear. The first modern toilet tissue was produced in the state of New Jersey in 1857 by a man named Joseph Gaetti. Sold in packets of 500, each sheet of this 'Therapeutic Paper', as it was called, was imprinted with Gaetti's name and impregnated with aloe to ease chaffing, a feature that is only now becoming common.

Just as a final note (in case you were wondering), the first time 'necessary paper' appeared on a roll was in 1890 and was produced by US manufacturer the Scott Paper Company.

7

Richard Gatling, Sir Hiram Maxim & the Machine Gun

If you were to quiz a group of military history buffs as to who invented the machine gun, their response might well depend on where they lived. Europeans would probably say Sir Hiram Maxim, while Americans would be more likely to offer the name of Dr Richard J Gatling. While both answers are, to some extent, correct, they are also equally wrong.

However strong their respective claims to the machine gun may be, it is interesting to note how much Maxim and Gatling had in common — they were both accomplished inventors who held multiple patents, they both worked during the second half of the 19th century and, despite Maxim's [1901] knighthood, they were both Americans. As to whether either of them can be credited with inventing the machine gun, let us first agree on the definition of the term 'machine gun'. If we accept as the only basic qualifications that it be a small-calibre weapon capable of firing multiple rounds of ammunition at a high rate of speed without reloading, then both Maxim and Gatling were Johnny-come-latelys to the field of mechanized slaughter.

The earliest attempts at producing an automatic gun, then known as a 'ribauldequin', amounted to little more than multiple small-bore cannon barrels clustered together and mounted on a wagon bed. The first recorded use of such a weapon took place in 1339 when the armies of England's Edward III were fighting the French. This particular gun contained 12 ranks of hand-cannon barrels, each rank holding 12 barrels. Whether they were fired a rank at a time, in volleys or individually is unknown, but considering the time necessary to reload all 144 barrels it is unlikely that the confusion of battle would have permitted more than a single firing.

The first major improvement in automated weaponry came about nearly a century and a half later when our old friend, Leonardo da Vinci, created three variations on the volley gun. Some time between 1480 and 1482 da Vinci wrote a letter to Ludovico il Moro in which he recommended himself as a military engineer. With his letter were included drawings of three multiple-firing guns (now in da Vinci's Codex Atlanticus, folio 157). One is a standard volley gun, another features a single rank of barrels arranged in a fan-shape to provide a wider field of coverage. The third design was probably the first step on the way to a true machine gun. The gun had three ranks of barrels with 11 barrels in each rank. Da Vinci had arranged each rank on a different face of a revolving, prism-shaped spindle. When one rank stood level with the enemy another faced downward and the third stood with its muzzles facing skyward, ready for reloading. We can assume that the ranks were revolved forward and downward so the guns had time to cool down before being reloaded.

It was a truly revolutionary idea, but given that the guns could not be reloaded during firing – and even with two men reloading it would have taken approximately five minutes to reload 11 barrels – the gun had an optimum fire-rate of 11 shots in six minutes.

We have no way of knowing if da Vinci's guns were ever built, but the conventional tiered volley gun remained a battlefield standard for well over two centuries – until the invention of the Puckle gun.

In May 1718 a London lawyer, notary-public and novelist named James Puckle received a patent for the first truly automatic weapon. The Puckle gun resembled a flint-lock musket with a revolving cylinder, not unlike those used on modern revolvers. Various models had from six to 12 chambers in the cylinder, carrying either 1¼ inch (32 mm) diameter musket balls or small shot. The great advantage of the Puckle gun over earlier volley guns was that it was tripod mounted and could be swivelled to change aim. Better still, with a fire-rate of up to nine shots per minute, the Puckle gun could out-fire three infantrymen. Unfortunately, it also had severe limitations. The cylinders of the gun had to be revolved by hand during operation, had to be removed to be reloaded, and required two or three men reloading if the fire-rate was to remain constant.

Everyone who witnessed Puckle's demonstration of his gun before government and military officials at the Woolwich Arsenal were duly impressed – everyone, that is, except the Government. For reasons unknown, the Government failed to place orders for the gun and Puckle was subsequently unable to find investors to help him market it abroad.

The Puckle gun may have been a commercial failure but his technology paved the way for other developments. The next advancement in automated weaponry, however, was some way off.

On 8 July 1856, Massachusetts native Charles E Barnes applied for a patent on what he called an 'automatic cannon'. From the description Barnes used in his patent application it would seem that this may have been the first attempt at a hand-cranked, self-loading machine gun. In the written description, Barnes talks about a mechanism that automatically feeds 'cartridges' into the firing mechanism. Considering that the metal cartridge had not yet been invented we are left to assume that these were the oiled paper cartridges (with gunpowder in one end and a musket ball in the other) commonly used in muskets of the period.

The gun may not have lived up to its promise, or there may simply have been no interest, but whatever the case, the Barnes automatic cannon never seems to have shown up in US military stores. Maybe it was just a case of Barnes having come along a bit too early.

There is nothing to spur the development of new and more terrible weapons like a good war, and within five years of Barnes' patent application the US would be caught in the grip of one of the bloodiest conflicts in human history – the American Civil War.

The first multi-fire gun to come out of the Civil War was designed even before the outbreak of hostilities. In 1860 – with tensions already running high – General Origen Vandenburgh of the New York State Militia designed a multi-barrelled volley gun not unlike the medieval ribauldequin, but now commonly referred to as an 'organ gun'. Vandenburgh's creation came in various calibres and models, having anywhere from 85 to a mind-boggling 451 barrels. Although still fired in volleys, the Vandenburgh gun was an improvement on its predecessors in that it featured rifled barrels, was breech-loading and was fired by a percussion cap. During tests the gun performed well; a 91-barrelled version of the Vandenburgh organ gun placed 90% of its rounds into a 6-foot diameter target at a distance of 100 yards (approximately 90 metres). Nonetheless, the US Government seemed completely uninterested, as did the British Government. Frustrated and angry, Vandenburgh sold his weapon design to the Confederacy. How this treacherous act impacted on his career with the Union Army is unknown.

Hard on the heels of open hostilities came such a flood of new weapons designs that we must investigate them not only by year, but by month.

In March 1861 Wilson Agar demonstrated his repeating rifle before a group of Union government dignitaries that included no less than President

Abraham Lincoln, and there is no doubt the Agar gun deserved its audience. It was not only the first hand-cranked, hopper-fed automatic weapon in history but was fitted with a steel shield to protect the gun and operator from enemy fire. Most interesting, though, was the ammunition. Although modern shell casings had not been invented, Agar designed a reusable metal cylinder to contain powder, ball and percussion cap. This feature, combined with the hand-cranked hopper-fed mechanism and an effective range of 1,000 yards (some 900 metres), made this a truly deadly machine (despite the drawback of requiring nearly a dozen men to fill sufficient shell casings to keep ahead of the firing). President Lincoln was so impressed with the gun that he placed an order for 10 on the day of the demonstration. Later, the Union Army would order an additional 44.

The first time the Agar gun is known to have seen action was in 1863 at the Battle of Middleburg (Virginia). Later, a Union officer who had been present recalled: 'One of these guns was brought to bear on a squadron of [Confederate] cavalry at 800 yards and it cut them to pieces.'

Still, the hopper feed mechanism was prone to jamming, and reloading the cartridges was so labour intensive that the Agar gun could not be said to be truly automatic.

In September of the same year (1861) an inventor from Kentucky named RS Williams devised another gun which took one more step on the long road to a fully automated weapon. Like the Agar gun, Williams' piece was hand cranked, but because it used the expended gases from each round to help open the breech, it had an effective fire-rate of 65 rounds per minute. Combine this with a range of 2,000 yards (just over 1,800 m) – fully twice that of the Agar gun – and it is small wonder that the Union Army ordered 45 of the weapons. Its major drawback was that, unlike the Agar gun, it still used paper cartridges, each of which had to be fed into the breech mechanism individually.

Despite being called a 'battery gun' (presumably because it had the fire-power of an entire infantry battery), the next big thing in American Civil War guns was a throw-back to the multi-barrelled ribauldequin. Patented by dentist Dr Josephus Requa in September 1862, the Requa battery gun was really nothing more than an improvement on da Vinci's gun of 380 years earlier. Rather than having three banks of rotating barrels, however, the Requa gun had a single row of 25, .52 calibre rifle barrels breech fed by a rotating drum fitted with eight rows of 'cartridges' fixed in place on the drum. As the drum was rotated a new row of loads advanced into place and was fired before the drum could be rotated again. Ignited with a single percussion cap, each row of 25 barrels fired simultaneously, thus providing a total of 200 shots before a new drum had to be set into place. It certainly would have produced a withering wall of lead, and 30 Requa battery guns were used in the siege of Charleston, South Carolina during the summer of 1863. Although it was mounted on an easily manoeuvered handcart, the gun lacked the ability to be swivelled during firing, limiting its effectiveness to bridges and narrow lanes.

All the components of a true machine gun were now available; some produced a high rate of fire, some could swivel and some could be automatically fed and crank fired. The only thing left was for someone to put all these variant pieces of technology together. Like Requa, that someone would be a dentist. His name was Dr Richard Gatling.

Born in 1818 in rural North Carolina, Gatling came from a family full of ideas. His father, Jordan, held two patents of his own, and Richard quickly followed in his footsteps. Although he studied medicine and dentistry, Gatling never found time to open a medical practice – he was too busy inventing things. Over the years he would invent plumbing devices, a rice-planting machine, bicycles, wool cleaners and other useful products – but it was his repeating gun that assured his place in history.

When war between the states broke out in 1861, Gatling was already 43 and too old to fight. He was not, however, too old to help the war effort. When he first demonstrated his gun to a group of military representatives in 1862 he claimed it would 'enable one man to do as much battle duty as a hundred'.

The Gatling gun included nearly all the best points of its predecessors. Like Agar's gun it fired purpose-made steel shell casings that had to be loaded by hand before being fed into the firing mechanism by a hand crank. But Gatling replaced Agar's hopper with a spring-loaded magazine, thus helping to eliminate the problem of jamming. Rather than using a single barrel, Gatling used a series of revolving barrels – numbering between six and 12, depending on the model – thus allowing each barrel to cool between firings. As each barrel had its own firing mechanism, the problem of overworking the mechanism was greatly reduced. Because it was swivel mounted, its field of fire could be changed at will despite the fact that the gun itself weighed in at a hefty 90 pounds (41 kg).

During its first public demonstration, the Gatling gun fired off an impressive 200 rounds per minute. Curiously, Brigadier-General JW Ripley, Chief of Ordnance for the Union Army, thought it was a waste of space. More precisely, he thought it was a waste of ammunition. In Ripley's world any soldier who fired more than three rounds per minute was just wasting bullets and money. Obviously, General Ripley had never been in battle. Another witness to the demonstration, General Benjamin Butler, saw matters differently and ordered 12 of Gatling's 10-barrelled guns with his own money. Later, Butler quipped that when he used the weapons on the Rebels they 'created great consternation'. Indeed, they must have. When Butler used the guns at the siege of Petersburg, Virginia in June 1864 he reportedly achieved a fire-rate of 1,000 rounds per minute and a range of 2,400 yards (2,194 m). This may have been an overstatement – 350 rounds per minute would have been more realistic – but the efficacy of the machine gun was now beyond dispute.

By 1867 Gatling had further improved his gun, eliminating a persistent gas leak by redirecting the expended gas into blowing open the breech to allow for faster firing. As factory-made, copper-jacketed shells had now come into production, he redesigned the gun to accommodate them and thus improve the gun's efficiency even more. At this point the US Government Department of Ordnance began placing orders for the Gatling gun. In 1870 Gatling moved his factory to Hartford, Connecticut where the gun was manufactured, under licence, by the Colt Armory. The next year the heavy wooden carriage was replaced by a metal tripod, allowing the gun greater manoeuverability. At a distance of 1,200 yards (1,097 m) the improved Gatling gun could sweep a 62 foot (19 m) wide front with a virtual wall of lead. By the early 1870s the Gatling gun was being used by nearly all the Western powers, both at home and in their far-flung colonial wars.

In 1881 a transplanted American inventor named Hiram Maxim left his adoptive home in England to visit the Paris Electrical Exhibition. While there he fell into conversation with a fellow American who observed that if a man wanted to become seriously rich all he needed to do was 'invent something that will enable these Europeans to cut each other's throats with greater facility'. It only took Maxim four years to live up to the challenge. In 1885 he demonstrated the world's first fully automated, portable machine gun. What Maxim did (that none before had accomplished) was to use the expended gas from each round not only to both blow open the breech and expel the empty cartridge but also to insert the next bullet into the firing chamber.

The first major action seen by this improved machine gun came during a British colonial conflict in Africa, known as the 'First Matabele War' (1893–94), when, in one memorable engagement, 50 British soldiers fought off 5,000 Ndebele warriors with just four Maxim guns. By the time of the Russo–Japanese war (1904–05), both the Russian and Japanese armies relied so heavily on the Maxim gun that nearly half of all casualties sustained in the conflict have been attributed to its gunfire.

8

Alexander Graham Bell & the Telephone

'Watson, come here, I want you!'

Anyone with a passing knowledge of the history of the telephone recognizes these words as having been spoken by Alexander Graham Bell to his assistant, Thomas Watson, on 10 March 1876, thus inadvertently proving that his experimental telephone actually worked. While the story and the quotation are probably true, whether or not Mr Bell can be given full credit for inventing the telephone is more in doubt.

In 1831 the great English scientist Michael Faraday had already discovered that electrical impulses, sent through a copper wire, would produce sound vibrations if one end of the wire was placed against a metallic disk. This alone made Faraday the world's then leading expert in sound transference.

In 1855 Faraday received a letter from a German schoolmaster and mathematics teacher named Philipp Reis, who asked the simple question: how could a single instrument reproduce at once the total actions of all the organs operated in human speech? To Faraday this may have posed an interesting puzzle, but to Reis it was a consuming question that had been worrying him for years.

Born three years after Faraday's first experiment with electrical sound transference, Reis had been interested in the wonders of electricity from childhood. At the age of 16 he was already an elementary school teacher, his restless mind consuming every scrap of scientific information he could lay his hands on. In 1851 Reis joined the Frankfurt Physical Society, a group dedicated to inquiring into the latest advances in science around the world. Among the group's honorary members was no less than Michael Faraday (also head of London's august Royal Institution), and many of Faraday's learned papers and articles were read aloud at meetings of the Frankfurt Physical Society. It was in response to one of these papers that Reis wrote to Faraday asking about the possibility of a machine capable of transferring human speech along an electric wire.

Reis had already been contemplating such a possibility, and his letter to Faraday was simply another step in trying to unravel the puzzle. Within two years of this correspondence, Reis had decided to construct a mechanical model of the human ear. Working in a shed in his back garden, Reis assembled an unlikely array of odds and ends. There were coils of wire, a knitting needle, the body of an old violin, a pile of corks and a length of pig-gut sausage casing. To reproduce the eardrum Reis stretched a piece of sausage skin across a hollowed-out cork, much like a small drumhead.

Imperceptibly close to this 'eardrum' Reis placed the end of a length of platinum wire. The proximity of the wire to the sausage skin was critical; it had to be close enough that even the slightest vibration in the skin would produce contact with the wire, but not so close that contact was constant. Reis hoped that as the improvised 'eardrum' vibrated it would create a series of short, intermittent contacts with the platinum wire, making and breaking an electrical circuit. The opposite end of the wire was wound around a knitting needle which had been mounted vertically onto the violin body. Reis believed that when electrical impulses reached the wire coil it would cause the violin to vibrate and reproduce whatever sound had been transferred along the wire.

It took two years of false starts to perfect this crude device, but in 1860 Reis ran 320 feet (some 100 metres) of wire from the sausage casing microphone in his shed to the violin speaker located in the nearby Garnier Institute, where he was now teaching. While one of his students stood near the violin, Reis placed his mouth close to the artificial eardrum and spoke the words: 'The horse eats no cucumber salad.' It may not have been as dramatic as 'Watson, come here, I want you!', but the student had understood every word. According to Reis' analysis of the experiment, 'The consonants are for the most part tolerably distinctly reproduced, but the vowels not yet in an equal degree.'

Calling his device *'Das Telephon'*, Reis worked for another year to improve sound reproduction before broadcasting news of his invention to anyone who cared to listen. On 26 October 1861 he demonstrated the device – the violin having been replaced by a sound box – to the Frankfurt Physical Society. Anxious to prove the viability of his 'phone', Reis disseminated construction plans to several recognized experts in the field of electrical transmission, including Wilhelm von Legat, Inspector of the Royal Prussian Telegraph Corps.

Despite having proven his device in front of both peers and government officials, Reis could not find a scientific journal willing to publish his work. Frustrated, but not discouraged, in 1862 and '63 he arranged for demonstrations across continental Europe and in Great Britain. Among those who saw, or acquired, *Das Telephon* were the London Science Museum, the British Association for the Advancement of Science, the Manchester Literary and Philosophical Society, Emperor Franz Josef and King Maximilian of Bavaria. By 1864 Reis had won over even the most hard-core doubters but, for reasons which remain obscure, fascination with the curious talking box quickly faded. However, before the chimera of fame fled, *Das Telephon* had been demonstrated in New York, where it was unquestionably seen by Thomas Edison and, quite possibly, by William Orton, President of Western Union Telegraph Company, and Alexander Graham Bell. Documentary evidence exists that a critical analysis of Reis' device, which appeared in the German publication *Polytechnisches Journal*, was translated into English for

Orton, and he passed it on to Edison (who was a friend and associate of Alexander Bell).

Reis' involvement in the invention of the telephone ends here, because in 1874 he died of tuberculosis aged 40. The story, however, continued to twist and turn for many years before Bell became directly involved.

While Reis had been working on his version of the telephone, so had an Italian theatrical technician named Antonio Meucci. Born in Florence in 1808, Meucci emigrated to Cuba in 1835 when offered the job of technical director for Havana's Teatro Tacón. Although a technician by trade, Meucci was a dedicated inventor at heart. In his first 10 years in Cuba he completely revamped Havana's waterworks (vastly improving the filtration system), established the first electro-plating factory in the Western Hemisphere and invented an improved system of electrotherapy, then an accepted form of medical treatment for a vast range of ailments.

In 1849, while administering an electrotherapy treatment to a patient, Meucci distinctly heard the sound of his patient's voice being transmitted over a copper wire attached to the therapeutic machinery. Realizing the possibilities in such a discovery – more than a decade before Reis' experiments achieved the same result – Meucci quit his job and moved his family to Staten Island, New York where he believed the commercial possibilities of such an invention could be best exploited.

While trying to establish himself in his new country, Meucci encountered several major problems.

First was creating a cash flow, and second was his inability to cope with the English language. In Cuba, due to the similarities between Spanish and Italian, Meucci had been able to gloss over his linguistic limitations, but now, in America, he became reliant on friends to serve as translators. Socially isolated, Meucci forged ahead with his work, spending more time than he would have liked developing non-related ideas in order to keep his family housed and fed. Over a period of 10 years he invented the first effective paraffin candles (these were previously made from smelly tallow extract), established a candle-manufacturing plant, patented a smoke-free kerosene lamp, discovered how to manufacture paper from wood pulp rather than rags, established the first paper mill to utilize recycled paper and invented carbonated drinks. In each case he was forced to entrust the running of his various enterprises to people who were fluent in both Italian and English. Through it all Meucci dedicated every free minute to his telephone.

By 1856, just six years after arriving in America, Meucci had made some significant advances with his device. Meucci's phone differed from Reis' in that it employed an electromagnet to improve the flow of electrical impulses, and the diaphragm (or eardrum) was stiffened with dichromate of potash and had a small iron button glued to the centre which helped control the vibrations, making the sound clearer.

In 1860 (the year prior to Reis' first public demonstration of *Das Telephon*), Meucci sent a model of his phone to Italy with a friend who was instructed to obtain financial backing for development and commercialization. Knowing that every idea must be published if it is to gain acceptance in the scientific community, Meucci described his device in New York City's Italian language newspaper, *L'Eco d'Italia*. Working through a translator, he held public displays of his machine in New York. Here, with typical Italian flair, he placed a singer in one room while her audience listened to her recital, telephonically, several rooms away. Although the demonstrations in the US and Italy were greeted with enthusiasm and wonder, they failed to provide the hoped-for funding. Even when he took in two business partners, all Meucci could generate was a measly $20.

If his finances were already strained, they were about to become a whole lot worse.

In 1861 several of Meucci's business managers joined forces with his unscrupulous lawyer and siezed control of virtually all his business ventures. Forced to take whatever work he could find, Meucci had to abandon plans for exploiting his telephone. His experiments, however, continued. To test innovations Meucci wired his house and workshop with phones. In August of 1870 he reportedly managed to transmit a clear telephone message over a distance of a mile – a major accomplishment considering the technology of the time. Now confident that he could find monetary backing, Meucci began making periodic trips from Staten Island into Manhattan to rekindle interest in his device. While returning home on the ferry *Westfield* one day in July 1871 the ship's boiler exploded killing many passengers and crew, and severely injuring Meucci.

Now unable to work, and faced with a mountain of hospital bills, the Meucci family entered perilous financial straits. In an attempt to generate even the smallest amount of cash, Mrs Meucci sold her jewellery, then the household furniture and paintings, and finally the working models of virtually all of her husband's inventions – including every telephone in the house – to a second-hand dealer for the grand sum of $6.

When Meucci was released from the hospital several months later he tracked down the junk dealer but was told that the telephones had been sold. As to the identity of the young man who had bought them, the second-hand dealer had not asked and did not care. Frantic to recreate his invention, the still-recovering Meucci worked constantly to rebuild the telephone and redraw all the plans necessary to prove how it was built. He was also desperate to obtain a patent on his device before someone else did; someone like the unknown young man who had purchased his models. Unable to raise the $250 required for a patent application, Meucci managed to scrape together $20 to file a 'patent caveat'; essentially a letter explaining the applicant's invention and their intention to file for a full patent at some future date. Under the terms of the caveat, should anyone apply to patent a similar invention, the holder of the caveat would be notified and given three months in which to file a full patent application themselves. Only if they failed to do so would the subsequent application be taken under consideration. The caveat could be renewed indefinitely, for a fee of $10 a year.

With this safety cushion in place, Meucci tried once more to drum up sufficient financial backing to make his device commercially viable. Among those he approached in 1872 was Edward B Grant, Vice President of the American District Telegraph Company, a wholly-owned subsidiary of Western Union. Certain the device would work at a far greater distance than the single mile he had already achieved, Meucci requested permission to attach the telephone to Western Union's endless miles of telegraph lines. To encourage the curiously reluctant Grant, Meucci even left a model of his device with American District's offices.

For two years, on an almost weekly basis, Meucci contacted Grant's office, but always received the same reply – Mr Grant was too busy to arrange the test; maybe next time. Finally, in desperation, Meucci demanded that Grant return his prototype but, as in the case of the second-hand dealer, the telephone had disappeared, and nobody seemed to know where. Virtually destitute and emotionally crushed, by 1874 Meucci found himself unable to come up with the $10 necessary to renew the patent caveat, and consequently let it lapse. Did this leave the field open for Bell? It would have, except for the existence of Elisha Gray, a partner in Gray & Barton Co, yet another subsidiary of Western Union Telegraph Company.

Born of Quaker parents on a small farm in Ohio in 1835, Gray was, like the other 'inventors' of the telephone, an inveterate tinkerer. At the age of 10 he built a working model of Morse's telegraph and went on to spend two years studying science at Oberlin College. At the age of 30, Gray invented a 'self-adjusting' telegraph relay that compensated for fluctuating signal strength. Four years later he went into partnership with Enos Barton, a budding entrepreneur who funded their enterprise by convincing his mother to mortgage the family farm. Together, Gray and Barton quickly won a contract to supply equipment to Western Union, which bought one third of Gray & Barton, shifted the company to Chicago, and changed the name of the satellite company to Western Electric Manufacturing Company (parent firm of the present-day Western Electric).

Although Gray soon retired from Western Electric to take up a teaching position with his *alma mater*, Oberlin College in Ohio, he remained the company's chief inventor. Precisely when Gray began developing his telephone remains obscure, but his first display of a sound-transmitting device took place at the Presbyterian Church of Highland Park, Illinois on 29 December 1874. This mechanism, which he called an 'Electric Telegraph for Transmitting Musical Tones', was effectively the first electronic synthesizer. From there it was but a short step to similarly reproducing the human voice. Considering Gray's familiarity with electronics, it seems almost inconceivable that he was unaware of Reis' telephone before embarking on the creation of his own. However it came about, on 14 February 1876 Gray's lawyer, William Baldwin, submitted a patent caveat, similar to the one filed by Meucci five years previously, but which had expired at the end of 1874. Had Meucci's caveat still been in effect he would have been notified of Gray's submission and given the chance to file a full application himself.

So convinced was Gray that he was the only contestant in the field, he opened his caveat with the statement: 'Be it known that I, Elisha Gray... have invented a new art of transmitting vocal sounds telegraphically...' Unique to Gray's version of the phone was a liquid-filled microphone, but beyond that detail it was very similar to the versions of both Reis and Meucci; not so much that fraud or theft is implied, but enough to make it clear that Gray had re-invented the wheel – probably after having seen one roll past!

The sequence of events at the US Patent Office that morning has become the stuff of legend. Supposedly, only two hours earlier, an almost identical application had been submitted by one Alexander G Bell, and it was by those 120 minutes that Gray lost one of the most lucrative inventions in history.

The legend, however, may be just that – a legend. It seems that Gray's attorney actually reached the Patent Office slightly more than two hours *before* Bell's lawyers, but – as so often happens in vast bureaucracies – the patent clerk took the caveat and Gray's money, laid them with a pile of other submissions on his desk, and went about his work, leaving the book-keeping until later. When Bell's lawyers, Anthony Pollok and Marcellus Bailey, arrived at the Patent Office they demanded that their client's application be processed immediately. As a result, although Gray's caveat had arrived earlier than Bell's, it was not entered into the ledger until several hours later.

But why were Pollok and Bailey in such a great hurry? Before answering this question we need to look at the story behind Bell's telephone.

Born and raised in Edinburgh, Scotland Bell came from a family where sound was of supreme importance. His father, Alexander Melville Bell, was a teacher to the deaf who had developed 'visible speech', a system of teaching speech to those who could not hear. His mother, Elisa Symonds Bell, was an accomplished portrait painter but was, herself, deaf. After attending the University of Edinburgh, Bell transferred to University College, London where his father conducted special education classes. After graduation, Bell remained at University College to assist his father. In his spare time he researched sound and acoustics in an effort to help the deaf communicate with the world around them.

When the elder Bells emigrated to Canada in 1870 (a decade after both Reis and Meucci had produced working telephones), young Alexander, now aged 23, moved with them. Only one year later he moved again, this time to Boston, Massachusetts where he set up practice as a teacher to the deaf and continued his research into artificial means of transferring sound. In 1875 he teamed up with Thomas Watson, a mechanical electrician, and stepped up his drive to produce a means of reproducing the human voice electrically. If there had been impetus before, things had now become urgent. Bell had recently courted, and married, one of his deaf students, and any means he could find to communicate with his beloved wife and mother would be nothing less than a godsend.

At least some of Bell's investigations are well recorded. On 1 March 1875 he met with Joseph Henry, then head of the Smithsonian Institution in Washington, DC. During this meeting Henry showed Bell the working model of Philipp Reis' *Telephon* and explained how the mechanism worked. Bell was fascinated by the device which, Henry no doubt explained, had never been patented by Reis (who had died 14 months earlier). Racing back to his lab, Bell and Watson began to reproduce Reis' invention as closely as Bell could remember it.

The 28-year-old Bell submitted his patent application (via his lawyers Pollok and Bailey) 11 months later, on 14 February 1876. It is important to note that Bell's application does not state that this was a new invention, but is entitled 'Improvements in Electric Telephony and Telephonic Apparatus'. Certainly, in examining his patent application, one is struck by just how vague the description of the telephone is; hardly specific enough, in fact, to have allowed a patent issuance. At this point Bell recognized that Reis had gone before him, and he openly referred to Reis as the original inventor of the telephone in a paper entitled 'Researches in Electric Telephony', which he presented publicly in May 1876, and again in October 1877.

Curiously, the incident where Bell said 'Watson, come here, I want you!' did not occur until 10 March 1876, nearly a month after he had applied for the patent, and three days after it had been granted. How could Bell have 'discovered' that his phone worked after he had already submitted the patent application and drawings? This question is not posed to imply that Bell was a fraud. Indeed, Bell went on to make a string of useful and innovative advances, including improvements to telephone technology and Edison's phonograph, the creation of the selenium cell battery and laying the groundwork for the development of fibre optics. In all, he patented 18 inventions, 12 of which he shared with other inventors. He was also instrumental in founding the National Geographic Society and was the recipient of numerous international awards.

But for all these honours we are left with the nagging question: how could Bell not have developed a working telephone until after the patent award? Certainly the editors of the respected journal *Scientific American* saw nothing new in Bell's accomplishment. In their issue dated 10 February 1877, in an article entitled 'The Speaking Electric Telegraph', they state: 'The articulating telephone of Mr Graham Bell, like those of Reis and Gray, consists of two parts, a transmitting instrument and a receiver'. Obviously, the same point occurred to Meucci and Gray.

Furious at Bell's seeming arrogance, and in spite of the contrary advice of his lawyer, William Baldwin, to bow to Bell's supposed two-hour lead on submitting his patent application, Gray now filed for a full patent application on his own telephone. Taking a more direct course, Meucci simply filed suit against Bell, claiming prior rights to any and all profits from the sales of the device. To encourage as much publicity as possible, Meucci also fired off a series of letters to every newspaper that would print them. These two actions were only the opening salvoes in what was to become one of the longest battles ever to drag its blood-soaked carcass through the US legal system.

To comprehend fully the scale of the fracas, the reader must understand that Bell was now head of the Bell Telephone Company and had considerable resources of his own. Gray was still employed as a consultant by Western Electric, and had not only that organization to back him up but also the nearly bottomless pockets of the firm's parent company, Western Union Telegraph Company, and its owners, financier JP Morgan and the Vanderbilt family. By September 1878 all sides had filed their suits and were deploying platoons of well-armed lawyers onto the field of battle.

Among the most damaging allegations to come out of the trial – although hearsay in nature, and subsequently discounted – was the claim that US Patent

Examiner Zenas Wilber had allowed Bell's attorneys to see Gray's caveat application and make notations on Bell's application that would have vastly improved the working of his telephone. Certainly the phone on which Bell uttered the immortal words 'Watson, come here, I want you!' did not have the same construction or design as the one which he had so vaguely described in his application just a few weeks earlier. Indeed, the device described in Bell's patent application would hardly have reproduced any sound at all.

The crime of patent fraud was not attributed to Bell himself but to his lawyers; still, the mud quickly rubbed off on Bell. It was also alleged that Gray's lawyer leaked technical information on Gray's superior device directly to Pollok and Bailey. Certainly, Bell's first working phone had utilized a liquid transmitter very like the one Gray had invented (and which was not included in Bell's patent application design).

In an attempt to salvage the situation, Bell offered Western Union a 20% share of all profits from his telephone for a period of 17 years, if they would drop their case against him. While out-of-court settlements are perfectly legal, it did nothing to enhance his image.

While Gray and Western Electric gnawed away at Bell, so did Antonio Meucci. In three separate law suits – one filed by Meucci, one by the Globe Telephone Company (now using Meucci's phones) and one by the US Government on Meucci's behalf – Bell, and his claim to having invented the telephone, were slowly taken apart.

Meucci's case, however, collapsed, and he died in October 1889 at the age of 81. By this time, however, most of the battles had already shifted from private law suits to government-sponsored ones. On 14 January 1886, Lucius Lamar, the United States Secretary of the Interior, drafted a letter to John Goode, US Attorney General, recommending that the US Government sue both the Bell Telephone Company and Alexander Graham Bell. Attached to the letter were no fewer than 60 documents which had been used as exhibits during one or more of the private law suits against Bell. Slowly, tortuously, the suits wound their way through the system; the Government's case advancing all the way to the US Supreme Court. When the Supreme Court handed down its decision on 19 March 1888, Alexander Graham Bell was exonerated of patent fraud by a single vote.

Bell or his company would eventually be involved in no fewer than 600 legal actions, the last case limping to its conclusion some 20 years after the fiasco began.

Near the close of the proceedings, William Orton, President of Western Union Telegraph Company, who had likely seen Reis' telephone demonstrated in New York in 1864, quipped: 'I find it amusing that Bell is perceived as the man who spent his whole fortune defending his patent on the phone when, in fact, what he did was spend his whole fortune patenting Philipp Reis' work.' How curious then that most of us still remember Bell as the inventor of the telephone.

Long after the participants in this grisly little epic had passed on to their final reward (or punishment, as the case may be), their cause still manages to raise occasional anger in public circles. What little recognition remained for Philipp Reis by the beginning of the 20th century was expunged not once but twice. When the Nazis came to power in Germany in 1932 the Ministry of Propaganda ordered Reis' name to be struck from every textbook and scientific treatise in the Reich. Why? Because Philipp Reis happened to be Jewish. But the Nazis routinely swept aside disagreeable truths; surely the rest of us wouldn't be so petty? In 1947 engineers from the British firm Standard Telephones and Cables examined Reis' 1863 telephone that had been in the collection of the London Science Museum since its construction. The results of their tests concluded that the mechanism could 'reproduce speech of good quality but of low efficiency'. Allegedly, on the order of Sir Frank Gill (then head of Standard Telephones and Cables), the results of these tests were suppressed. Why? Perhaps because Standard Telephones were then in negotiations with AT&T (inheritors of the Bell Telephone Company), and Gill feared that admitting what Bell himself had acknowledged three-quarters of a century earlier – that Reis' phone worked – might damage relations between the two. The results of the 1947 tests were not widely released until late in 2003.

Eventually, Antonio Meucci was granted recognition for his work. In September 2001 the US Senate passed a resolution stating that Antonio Meucci, an Italian by birth and an American by naturalization, had invented the telephone. Ten months later the US House of Representatives passed a similar resolution. Elisha Gray still remains the man who submitted his patent caveat two hours late, even though in all probability he put it in two hours prior to Alexander Graham Bell.

9

Thomas Edison & the Electric Light

The story of Thomas Edison, and how he came to invent the light bulb, is so well known that it nearly transcends history and enters the realm of legend.

Young Tom was never a good student and dropped out of school after only three months, whereafter he was taught at home by his mother. Because the family was poor, Tom went to work at the age of 12 when he started selling newspapers at the local railway station. On one occasion, as punishment for some minor infraction, his boss boxed Tom's ears, inadvertedly rupturing his eardrum and leaving him partially deaf; but even this did not deter the lad. Later, when the stationmaster's son wandered onto the tracks, Tom heroically saved the youngster from an oncoming train. As a reward he was given a position in the telegraph office, where he soon became a whizz at telegraphy and invented a relay system that allowed messages to be forwarded automatically from one telegraph station to the next. Eventually, using the money he had made from a series of telegraph-related inventions, Edison set up his own little inventor's shop where, after first inventing the phonograph, he toiled away on inventing an electric light. It took many years (and literally thousands of false starts) but finally, in 1879, Thomas Edison brought illumination to a dark world.

There is, of course, some truth to this story; but like all legends the tale has been somewhat exaggerated and edited for the benefit of its hero.

Before continuing, let us determine exactly what an electric light is. In its simplest form, an electric light is nothing more than a dead short in an electrical circuit. At the point where the circuit is broken the current builds up, generating heat. If there is a mechanism available to capture the built-up power the heat will cause it to glow. The principle is eminently simple; so simple, in fact, it would seem that almost anyone with access to electrical current could build one. Not surprisingly, almost everyone did.

The first component to the electric light – electrical power – was captured around 1800 by Italian scientist Alessandro Volta in the form of a wet-cell battery, not very different from the ones still found in automobiles. In this great age of scientific 'curiosities' Volta held innumerable public displays of his battery – which he called an 'electric pile' – during which he attached copper wires to the positive and negative terminals, brought the wires close together and produced a brief flash of light in the form of an electrical spark.

Building on Volta's discovery, that same year a 22-year-old English chemist, physician and experimenter named Sir Humphry Davy passed the electrical current from one of Volta's batteries through a carbon rod and discovered that it glowed intensely until it finally ignited, much like burning charcoal. When Davy substituted a thin strip of platinum for the carbon rod he found he could sustain the glow much longer – at least until the platinum ribbon melted. Sir Humphry tried to extend the life of his lights by enclosing them in a glass tube from which the air had been extracted, but the vacuum pumps of the time could not extract sufficient air to prevent the platinum from melting or the carbon from bursting into flame. Eventually, he experimented with two short carbon rods, separated by a small air space, and discovered he could produce a brilliant white light that could be maintained for as long as the battery held out. This was the first carbon-arc light, and while it was fascinating, even Davy admitted he was baffled by how electricity actually worked, noting: 'In the present state of knowledge, it would be useless to attempt to speculate on the remote cause of the electrical energy'.

Most of Davy's experiments, and the associated public demonstrations, centred around the properties and effects of a variety of gases. The most popular demonstrations seem to have centred around nitrous oxide, commonly known as 'laughing gas', and eventually Davy became addicted to the giggling vapour. At some point (around 1802) Davy passed an electrical current through a glass tube filled with one of his gases and produced a much softer light than the carbon arc. This first fluorescent light was appropriate to indoor use, but its life was still limited by the power of the battery. The technology did not yet exist for producing a constant, reliable electric light, but Davy had unquestionably created not only the first artificial light but had also invented the carbon-arc light and the gas-filled light which today exist as fluorescent, neon and mercury vapour lamps.

In 1835, only six years after Davy's death at age 51, a doughty Scotsman named James Lindsay carried out an amazing demonstration of his own electric light at Dundee in Scotland. An incorrigble tinkerer, inventor and scientist, Lindsay produced an artificial light of sufficient strength that even in a darkened room he could easily read a book at a distance of 18 inches away from it. Amazing as this feat was, Lindsay did not continue his experiments in lighting and soon moved on to other pursuits. It was only six years before Frederick de Moleyns took up the banner.

Basing his work on the experiments of fellow Englishman Davy, de Moleyns devised a light bulb in which the filament comprised finely powdered charcoal sandwiched between two platinum strips and housed inside a glass globe from which the air had been extracted. The effectiveness of this bulb is assured because in 1841 – nearly 40 years before Edison was granted his patent – de Moleyns was granted a British patent for the first incandescent light bulb.

But developing a better artificial light source, or new and inventive uses for electricity, was not limited to

British shores. A conjurer named Jean-Eugène Robert-Houdin (after whom Harry Houdini would later take his stage name) was already standing all of France on its collective ear with his electrically-based magic tricks when, in 1851, he gave a public demonstration of a light bulb not dissimilar to the one devised by de Moleyns.

It was not, however, until a decade later that electric lighting began to move out of the realm of scientific curiosity and into mainstream technology. This shift came largely through the efforts of Joseph (later Sir Joseph) Wilson Swan.

A physicist, chemist and inventor, Swan worked for a chemical company but spent nearly all of his spare time researching the latest scientific advances, among which was the now 50-year-old chain of experiments into electric lighting. When not inventing things like dry-plate photography, Swan constantly experimented with ways to make the light bulb practical. By the late 1840s, Swan (then only in his early 20s) was already devising a bulb that utilized a carbonized paper filament strung between two copper wires and suspended inside a glass sphere, from which the air had been extracted. It took a full 10 years to perfect the device, but in 1860 Swan obtained a patent for his improved light. Unfortunately, the light was still far from practical. Because vacuum pumps of the day had changed little over the past half century, enough oxygen-rich air remained in the bulb to allow the carbon filament to smoulder and blacken the inside of the globe after only a few hours' use.

Understanding the nature of the problem, but equally aware that there was nothing he could do about it, Swan turned his attention back to his job at the chemical company, where he investigated ways of producing thread from various plant fibres. Meanwhile, the problem of a practical light continued to plague inventors all over the world.

In 1872 Alexander Lodygin, a Russian electrical engineer, applied for a patent for a light bulb in which the filament, suspended inside a heavy bell jar, was made from an extremely thin carbon rod. While Lodygin's light was too cumbersome for domestic use – and homes had no electrical power anyway – it turned out to be ideal for use on ships, whose engines could generate the necessary power. Lodygin immediately set about patenting his device in Austria, Britain, France and Belgium, making a tidy profit in the process.

In the same year Lodygin was granted his Russian patent (1874), two young Canadians were also involved in what now seemed an almost universal craze. When medical student Henry Woodward began lodging at the hotel of Mathew Evans the two discovered they shared a love of experimenting with electricity. Since Woodward had a battery and an induction coil they wiled away their spare time making things buzz and spark. Undoubtedly one, if not both, of the pair kept up with the latest developments in the world of electricity, and it was only a matter of time before they tried to build an electric light. For the globe they used the glass tube from an old water guage and into this they inserted two electrodes separated by a thin piece of high quality carbon. The ends of the guage were sealed, but a petcock was installed into one of the plugs so the air could be pumped from the tube. The extracted air was then replaced with nitrogen gas. The lamp's light was feeble, but it had a relatively long life and Woodward and Evans were granted a Canadian patent for it in 1874. Having no intention of going into the electric lighting business, Woodward and Evans did what many independent inventors do – they looked for someone to buy their patent.

While some inventors worked on the incandescent bulb, others were just as dedicated to the exploitation of Davy's carbon-arc light. One of these was Charles F Brush.

Born on an Ohio farm in 1849, by the time he was 12, young Charles was already hooking things up to electric batteries, and before he was 30 he had developed a fully functional carbon-arc lamp designed for outdoor use. Because he worked for Cleveland, Ohio's Telegraph Supply Company, Brush was able to arrange a public display of his light on Cleveland's Public Square. In April 1879 Brush and a group of workers from Telegraph Supply erected a dozen lamps around the perimeter of the square and connected them, not to a series of batteries but to an electrical generator Brush had devised three years earlier. The generator was a crude affair powered by a chugging, puffing steam engine salvaged from an old threshing machine and now housed in the Telegraph Supply

Company's nearby warehouse; but when the crowd gathered on the evening of 29 April 1879 they saw something no one had ever seen before. With the flick of a switch Charles Brush banished the darkness. Not only had he perfected the carbon-arc lamp, he had created a power source to run it.

Within the year Wabash, Indiana became the first town in the world to have electrically-powered street lights. Wabash was quickly followed by New York, Boston, Cleveland, Philadelphia, Baltimore, Buffalo, San Francisco and Montreal, Canada.

Despite its immediate success, the carbon-arc light was not suitable for indoor use; its light was simply too bright and too glaring for the interior of people's homes. Not to worry. While Brush was developing his light, Joseph Swan had been able to return to his own experiments thanks to the development of an improved vacuum pump. Having switched from a carbonized paper filament to one made from carbon-impregnated thread, he found that the near-perfect vacuum allowed him to produce a bright, clear light that neither blackened the inside of the bulb nor burned out in a few hours. Brush immediately applied for another patent – which he would be granted in 1879 – but continued to search for an improved filament. What he eventually discovered was that a thread of the artificial fibre called cellulose (which he had developed for his employer) proved to be the perfect replacement for carbonized thread. Tough and resilient to the electric current passing through it, this polymer-like substance was an ideal resistor – it glowed but was not consumed. In 1879 Swan began installing electric lighting in homes and public buildings around England, and the next year he held the world's first large-scale public display of functional, incandescent lighting in the city of Newcastle-upon-Tyne and lodged a patent application in the United States.

Since Alessandro Volta and Humphry Davy's first experiments into the generation of artificial light 80 years earlier, more than two dozen inventors had produced some kind of functional light bulb. So what had Thomas Edison been doing all this time?

Edison had, as we learned at the start of this chapter, invented a telegraph relay. He had also invented a device that allowed multiple messages to be sent simultaneously along the same telegraph wire, and an improved stock-ticker – a machine that continuously printed stock quotations on a narrow band of paper tape. Together, Edison's early inventions had netted him a healthy profit of $40,000 and brought him to the attention of investors in New York City.

With cash in hand (and the financial backing of Wall Street), Edison established a research facility at Menlo Park, New Jersey. Here, in addition to vastly improving Bell's telephone and inventing the phonograph, he made what is perhaps his most important contribution to science – he invented the research laboratory. Tom Edison was no lone inventor toiling away in a shed in his back garden; he was a clever man who knew that there was a far larger market out there than he could ever exploit by himself. To that end he gathered together a team of engineers, craftsmen, chemists and other eager young minds and put them to work – not necessarily inventing new things but making improvements on dozens of products that already existed. Inevitably, when someone who worked for Edison's company made a discovery, the credit (along with the patent rights and profit) went to the boss.

By the mid-1870s Edison knew that the next big money-spinner would be the electric light. Thanks to his research team, he also knew exactly who had made how much progress towards developing the goose that would lay this particular golden egg.

When he was shown an 1874 Canadian patent filed under the names of Henry Woodward and Mathew Evans, Edison sent his lawyers out to purchase a 50% share in the patent rights. Sensing the barbarians at his gate, Woodward immediately went out and filed for an American patent on the same invention. Edison now had no choice but to buy up this second patent in its entirety, which he did in 1879.

It was not as though Edison had much room to manoeuvre. A year earlier, in 1878, he had formed the Edison Electric Light Company (with substantial backing from financiers JP Morgan and the Vanderbilt family) and announced to the world that he, Thomas Edison, had invented the world's first functional electric light. In reality, he had not even begun working on the problem. Once he had Woodward's Canadian patent, however, he set his entire staff to work perfecting the bulb. He built his own glass factory and sent letters to every botanist and biologist he could find in search of the best possible material to create a long-lasting filament. Edison himself remarked: 'I tested no fewer than 6,000 vegetable growths and ransacked the world for the most suitable filament material.' When he tried to reproduce Swan's filament of carbonized thread he found he had a filament that would glow for a full 15 hours before burning out – but that was hardly long enough to make the Edison bulb marketable.

It was not until late autumn 1879 that Edison possessed a bulb that would burn for 1,500 hours before the filament went, and in December of that year he held the first public display of the new bulb by illuminating his research complex at Menlo Park. All Edison had to do now was invent an entire infrastructure so the light bulb would be a commercially viable product. To his credit, he did exactly that. Over the next seven years Edison's staff designed parallel circuitry, improved the bulb still further, improved the design of Charles Brush's dynamo-generator, developed an underground conductor network and voltage regulators, created safety fuses to control the flow of electricity into homes and came up with the first electrical sockets and on/off switches. Edison also bought out the remaining half of Woodward and Evans' Canadian patent. On 4 September 1882, Tom Edison personally switched on the world's first commercial power station and illuminated the homes and offices of 59 customers on the southern tip of Manhattan Island. It was, by any measure, a monumental achievement, but Edison had done little of the actual work himself and, while most of the world believed otherwise, he had certainly not invented the light bulb.

There were, of course, those who were not happy about Edison's claims. High on this list was Joseph Swan. Swan, like dozens of others whose work on some facet of the long-running light bulb story had seemingly been negated by Edison's claims, lined up to file suit against him. Edison fought tooth-and-claw to defend himself, but fact was not always on his side. The suit with Swan was settled when Edison agreed to merge his UK operation with Swan's company, creating what became known as 'Ediswan'. In a move that can be seen as small but sweet revenge, Sir Joseph Swan then sold the rights to his US patent – not to Edison but to Charles Brush and the Brush Electric Company. But Edison's problems were far from over. In 1883 the US Patent Office ruled that one of Edison's patents was based on a bulb designed, and previously patented, by a man named William Sawyer, and was therefore invalid.

This case, along with more than 500 others brought against Edison, dragged on until Edison finally managed to secure the ownership of at least one legitimate patent to the light bulb. Of course, he had purchased that particular patent from Henry Woodward.

Holding more US patents than any one else in history (1,093), and actually having invented a few useful things himself, Thomas Edison was a pretty smart (though tough) operator. He worked his staff and colleagues relentlessly, gaining credit for their ideas. He did, however, create the concept of the modern research laboratory and built the infrastructure necessary to support a modern world which runs largely on electric power. But whatever he did, good or bad, he certainly did *not* invent the light bulb.

10

Karl Benz & the Automobile

Except for those still labouring under the tragic misconception that the automobile was invented by Henry Ford, most people will assert that our beloved gas-guzzler was created by the German engineer Karl Benz. While this is not precisely the case, Benz's story does bear repeating.

The son of a railroad engine driver, Benz was fascinated by mechanics, and how things can be made to move under their own power, throughout his life. Born in November 1844, by the time he was 15 Benz had enrolled in the Karlsruhe Technical University where he majored in mechanical engineering. In 1871, Benz and a business partner opened their own mechanical engineering works in Mannheim, Germany which (by 1883) had become Benz & Company. While the company churned out a string of mundane mechanical devices, Benz took on the role of chief engineer and, inventor, devoting much of his time to developing a motorized carriage. Mounting a benzene-fuelled internal combustion engine (based on the revolutionary four-stroke model designed by Nikolaus Otto) onto a light, tubular-framed, three-wheeled carriage, Benz took the first test drive in his new 'velocipede' in August of 1885. Convinced that he had a hit on his hands, Benz patented his device immediately. Eighteen months later he put a much improved version of the Benz *'Motorwagen'* on the market and waited for the orders to pour in.

Despite his car having an astounding number of innovations, including a vaporizing carburetor, a speed regulator, an accelerator, a battery-powered ignition system, a clutch, a gear shift and a water-cooled radiator, the public seemed remarkably uninterested in placing their orders. Possibly this was because another German firm, Daimler & Co, was now offering a four-wheeled version of the automobile at a price competitive with Benz's three-wheeler.

The Benz business might well have languished permanently had it not been for Karl's wife, Berta, who bundled up their two boys one balmy August afternoon in 1888, loaded them into the *Motorwagen* and set off for Pforzheim, over 60 miles (96 km) distant. Not only did the car make the trip without a single mechanical glitch, but *Mein Gott*, it had been driven by a woman! The publicity put Benz and his car permanently on the automotive map. But if Daimler had a car in production at the same time, and both of their engines had been designed by Otto, who really invented the car?

To answer this we must first define what constitutes an automobile. Must it have four wheels? Benz's only had three. Must it be fuelled by petrol (gasoline)? Benz's first experimental model ran on benzine. To help answer these questions let us define our terms. The word 'automobile' is derived from both Greek and Latin. The word *'auto'* in Greek means 'self' and the Latin word *'mobilis'* simply means 'moveable'; thus to qualify as an automobile a device only has to be self-propelled. For our definition we will also require that it is able to carry passengers and does not run on rails.

In 1870, 15 years before Karl Benz began assembling his first experimental car, Siegfried Marcus, a manufacturer of scientific instruments from Mecklenburg, Germany mounted a crude internal combustion engine onto a four-wheeled fruit peddler's handcart. It was an ungainly-looking creature, resembling nothing so much as a guillotine on wheels. Steering was virtually non-existent, but it ran, and Marcus jockeyed it through the streets of Mecklenburg for several years. By 1883, Marcus had moved to Vienna and improved his propulsion system by creating a magneto-powered, low voltage engine and, in 1889, he placed the new engine in a custom-made carriage now known as the 'Second Marcus Car'.

Although Marcus would go on to garner 131 patents of various kinds, his automotive enterprises had already been surpassed by both Benz and Daimler; nonetheless, awkward as it was, the 'First Marcus Car' was earlier than either. But Siegfried Marcus was still not the first in the automotive field.

A decade before Marcus, and a quarter of a century prior to Benz and Daimler, Jean-Joseph Étienne Lenoir of Belgium mounted a 5 horsepower, two-cycle coal–gas-powered engine (the type now common on lawn mowers, where petrol and oil are mixed together in the fuel tank) and used it to power a converted carriage. The vehicle must have been cumbersome in the extreme; the single-cylinder engine's bore was a full 5 inches, the piston had a stroke length of 24 inches and only turned over at the rate of 100 rpm. Lenoir's car may only have reached a top speed of 2 miles (*c.*3 km) an hour, and it may have taken him three hours to drive the 7 miles from midtown Paris to Joinville, but at least he had the road to himself.

Lenoir may never be remembered as the builder of the first car, which indeed he was not, but it seems he did produce the first functioning internal combustion engine; unless, of course, we consider François Isaac de Rivaz.

Of French–Spanish parentage, de Rivaz was born in Switzerland in 1752, and seems to have been a constant dabbler in all things mechanical. Throughout the last quarter of the 18th century he worked with the knotty problem of powering a carriage by steam. He did have some success at this, but it was not until 1807 that he hit on what would be his greatest contribution to science – an internal combustion engine. Low on power and high on weight, de Rivaz's first successful engine was fuelled by hydrogen. The de Rivaz engine may have been a bit sluggish, but it ran hot as a volcano. By 1813 he had worked out a basic gearing and drive system and mounted the engine on a custom-made chassis. At nearly 19 feet (almost 6 metres) in length, and tipping the scales at just over a ton, the de Rivaz car chugged its way along for more than 325 feet (some 100 m), each of the 25 firings of the single gigantic piston being set off by hand.

It was to de Rivaz, then, that we owe the creation of the internal combustion engine. But, as we have already established, a car's motive power is not necessarily what makes it a car.

James Watt invented the steam engine. Well, maybe he didn't, but we have already considered this issue in another chapter. He did, however, hold the British steam engine patent, and developing uses for steam power without having to give credit (and vast sums of money) to Watt made developing innovative uses for steam difficult in late 18th century Britain. At least until Watt's patent ran out in 1800.

For some years a Cornish mining engineer named Richard Trevithick had been playing around with possible applications for Watt's steam engine beyond pumping water from mine shafts, then its primary use. Installing one of the heavy engines onto the bed of a freight wagon, Trevithick and several friends made the perilous climb up one of Cornwall's steep hills late in 1801. Fortunately for the intrepid crew, at the top of the hill stood a welcoming pub. Less fortunately, when Trevithick pulled his smoke-belching machine into a shed, sparks from the smokestack promptly burned down the building, destroying the vehicle.

Not one to be discouraged by small set-backs, Trevithick promptly patented, and built, another, better steam carriage at the mind-boggling cost of £20. The new 'London Steam Carriage' of 1803 was a giraffe of a beast standing more than 14 feet (4 m) high. Sitting above the axles were the fire-box and boiler, and mounted at a safe height above this stood the body of a fine carriage. Towering above it all was the smokestack. Despite the fact that passengers had to scale a ladder to enter the seating compartment, the vehicle seemed to be a triumph. On its maiden journey it puffed its way through central London to Paddington, and skirted Islington, eventually carrying all eight passengers safely back to their starting point.

Precisely how many trips the London Steam Carriage made during its short life is unknown, but one evening Trevithick and his driver lost control of the creature, crashing it into a stone wall. The force of the impact destroyed the wall and toppled the juggernaut onto its side, spilling the terrified passengers into the street. There is no account of any serious injuries, but the authorities declared the beast unsafe and Trevithick was forced to take it to the scrapyard. The valiant boiler from London's first self-propelled steam carriage ended its days powering machinery that made hoops for beer barrels.

Whether or not he was aware of the fact, Trevithick was not the first man, nor indeed the first mining engineer working in Cornwall, to power a vehicle with a steam engine. Two decades earlier a Scotsman named William Murdock had been installing steam-powered pumps in the tin mines of Cornwall when he was struck by an almost identical idea. In 1784 Murdock had built a custom-made, three-wheeled vehicle that puffed its smoky way up and down the roads of Cornwall for several years before he abandoned the idea as a waste of time.

But even before Murdock, a French inventor named Nicolas-Joseph Cugnot had pioneered the idea of a steam-powered vehicle. Born in 1725 in the Meuse area of Lorraine, Cugnot became an army engineer who dedicated himself to devising better and faster methods of deploying artillery on the battlefield. Encouraged by his superior officers, Cugnot produced his first scale model of a steam-powered gun carriage around 1763. Having demonstrated this military toy to the satisfaction of the army and King Louis XV, in 1769 he produced the first full-scale version of his '*Fardier à Vapeur*' or 'Steam Dray'. The most innovative aspect of Cugnot's creation was a method for converting the back-and-forth, or up-and-down, motion of steam engines into the circular motion necessary to turn a wheel. James Watt would eventually recreate this feat, but it was Cugnot who did it first.

The Steam Dray itself was both massive and heavy. Looking like a three-wheeled locomotive engine, the boiler extended well beyond the single front wheel, which was steered by a tiller. Power was supplied to the rear wheels, which moved the thing forward, pulling up to four and a half tons of cannon behind it at a top speed of 2 miles per hour with apparent ease. If the Dray had a drawback it was that every 10 or 12 minutes it had to stop long enough to recharge the head of steam necessary for propulsion. Also, although it ran well with a host of cannon hitched to the back, when relieved of its burden the nose-heavy boiler tipped earthward, lifting its rear wheels off the ground. Suitably impressed with his accomplishment, the next year Cugnot set out to build an improved, passenger-carrying version of his creation.

Although the 1770 model of the Steam Dray still tended to be a touch nose heavy, and tipped the scales at an impressive 8,000 pounds (3,628 kg), it ran at fully twice the speed of its predecessor, sailing through the Paris streets at a hair-raising 4 miles an hour. Like Trevithick's London Steam Carriage of some 30 years later, however, there were difficulties with the steering mechanism. After only a few months on the road the Dray crashed into a wall, chalking up the world's first car crash. Still, even King Louis thought Cugnot had accomplished something worthwhile and awarded him a pension of 600 francs a year. Unfortunately, the pension disappeared with the onset of the French Revolution, and Cugnot was forced to flee the country (or risk the guillotine) for his services to the old military establishment. But Cugnot's wonderful Steam Dray survives and is now on display at the National Academy of Arts and Sciences (Conservatoire Nationale des Arts et Métiers) in Paris.

While Cugnot may have been the first actually to construct a steam-powered, passenger-carrying vehicle, he was not the first to envision one. As early as 1680 the great English mathematician Sir Isaac Newton suggested the possibility of such a creation, and sketched out plans for its construction. It was powered by a spherical steam turbine much like that designed by Hero of Alexandria in the first century AD (discussed in Chapter 2 of this book); Newton proposed propelling his machine by the force of a steam-jet escaping from a ventilator tube positioned at the rear of the boiler. It is unlikely that Newton's device would have possessed the propulsive power necessary to overcome inertia, and there is no evidence that a prototype was ever constructed, but all good ideas have to begin somewhere.

Of course, the limits of what constitutes an automobile are no more confined to steam propulsion than they are to petroleum distillates. As every automotive designer now working with electric and solar-powered cars knows, you don't have to burn something to make a car move. So, is it possible that some enterprising genius designed a car that would actually run long before rotary motion was first produced by a fuel-fired engine? It is if that someone happened to be Leonardo da Vinci.

Leonardo di ser Piero da Vinci would have been recognized as a genius no matter when he had lived. He was by turns a sculptor, architect, engineer, scholar and inventor of numerous devices, including flying machines, the military tank, the double-hulled ship and the submarine. Up until the late 19th century, however, he was known almost exclusively as the man who painted the *Mona Lisa*, *The Last Supper* and other great artistic works of the Italian Renaissance.

It was not much more than a century ago that a few Italian scholars began looking into, and releasing, the contents of the great man's surviving notebooks (most of which had disappeared, or were destroyed in the hands of the Church following his death in 1519). What emerged was the true extent of da Vinci's scientific genius. Among the several codexes (the name given to da Vinci's compiled sketches and notebooks) was found what is now known as folio 812r of the Atlantic Codex. Executed around 1478, 812r contained detailed sketches and notes for the construction of a motorized car.

What was evident from the drawings was that the three-wheeled, flat-bedded, wagon-like vehicle measured about 5 feet 6 inches in length and 5 feet in width (1.7 m x 1.5 m), was constructed primarily of wood and steered by a tiller attached to the single wheel located at the front. Also shown was a pair of large leaf-springs, arranged to look like a giant crossbow, which most scholars agreed was the source of the vehicle's motive power. By studying Leonardo's written notes and drawings they also determined that the mechanism worked much like a clock. To wind up the spring mechanism the wheels were wound backwards – the opposite direction from which they turned when the car was in motion. It was also clear that the rear wheels had differential gearing (like any modern automobile) and possessed a rudimentary braking system. What no one could figure out, however, was exactly how da Vinci had intended the motor to work. No surprise, perhaps – these academics were historians not engineers. What was needed was a body of people who knew almost as much about mechanical engineering as one man who had died more than four centuries earlier. That kind of knowledge, however, had to wait until the 21st century.

Beginning in 2002, a team of engineers, master carpenters, computer experts and da Vinci scholars joined forces to unravel the mysteries of the 'da Vincimobile'. With the aid of endless computer models they finally discovered that the huge leaf-springs did not actually provide power, they only controlled its release, rather like the regulating mechanism in a clock. The actual power was contained in a drum-enclosed main-spring. After eight months of study and toil a full-sized reconstruction of Leonardo's car went on display at Florence's Institute and Museum of the History of Science. Like so many of his far-sighted inventions, it is highly unlikely that Leonardo's car was ever built during his lifetime, and although it took 525 years to put it together, it does actually work. According to Paolo Galluzzi, Director of the Institute, not only does it work but it is 'a very powerful machine'.

Almost beyond belief is the fact that someone designed an automobile nearly 150 years before da Vinci. In 1335 another Italian Renaissance inventor named Guido da Vigevano devised what he called his 'Wind Wagon'. But this was no sailboat on wheels. The Wind Wagon was a carriage with a windmill-like device mounted above the passenger compartment. When facing into the wind the blades of the windmill turned a shaft which, in turn, provided power to a set of drive gears that turned the rear wheels. Probably never built at the time, and certainly never built since, computer engineers have put a CGI (computer-generated image) model of da Vigevano's car through its electronic paces and determined that, with a good headwind, the world's very first car could have reached speeds of up to 30 miles (48 k) per hour, a feat not achieved in actuality until the opening decade of the 20th century – more than 550 years after da Vigevano's death.

If neither Karl Benz nor Henry Ford invented the car, what then did Henry Ford do to make him so famous? One of the more popular beliefs surrounding Ford is that he built the first automobile in the US. In truth, Ford's first accomplishment was to build a fairly high-efficiency gasoline-powered engine. This he did in the spring of 1893, eight years after Karl Benz had test driven his first velocipede. Unfortunately for Ford, by the autumn of that same year – and fully three years before Ford set off down the road in his first car – brothers Charles and Frank Duryea were already tootling around their native Springfield, Massachusetts in a car that had four wheels (unlike Benz's three-wheeler), and which was powered by a standard petroleum derivative known as gasoline.

So there we have it, a brief history of when the first automobile appeared, and when it first reached the shores of the car-happy USA. Unless, that is, we consider the name of John Lambert of Ohio City, whom many historians now believe was the first American to build a car, in 1891. The case for Lambert remains shaky, but even without him we have only considered those Americans who built petrol-powered vehicles. In 1871 Dr JW Carhart, a physics professor teaching at Wisconsin State University, hired farm machinery company JI Case to construct a passenger-carrying, steam-powered buggy he had designed. The success of the vehicle is undoubted, and it made enough of a stir that the state of Wisconsin sponsored what may well have been the world's first car race in 1878. With a gruelling 200-mile course, and a generous prize of $10,000, there was no lack of entrants — seven of them, in fact, and all steam powered. In the event, only two entrants showed up, and the eventual winner (sponsored by the city of Green Bay, Wisconsin) won with a whopping average speed of 6 miles per hour.

But long before this great race there were Americans anxious to put their country on wheels. In 1789 Oliver Evans, a 34-year-old professional engineer and self-made inventor, designed a machine that used a traditional low-pressure boiler to drive a freight wagon that was powerful enough to move 100 barrels of flour from Lancaster, Pennsylvania over 80 miles (129 k) of pretty basic roads to Philadelphia in only two days (rather than the three required by traditional horse-drawn wagon). Immediately, Evans took out a patent on his device. Spurred by his success, in 1804 (about the time Trevithick's London Steam Carriage hit the roads)

Evans installed the first high-pressure steam engine onto a strange creation which looked something like a flat-bottomed boat.

As we have already seen, there had been steam cars in Britain and France earlier than this, but they used low-pressure boilers and thus produced far less motive force for their size than did Evans' car. Evans was also clever enough to realize that he could get more speed by using the pistons to *push* the wheels rather than pull them. To add even more innovations to his contraption, Evans installed a second propulsion system – a paddle wheel – at the rear of the vehicle. Evans had in fact been commissioned to build a dredging scow to clear the channel of a nearby river. Since his workshop was 16 miles (almost 26 kilometres) from the dredge site, Evans simply built a scow that could propel itself from his workshop to the site and back again. Before setting off for work that first morning in the early summer of 1805, Evans cruised merrily around the town square several times before driving to the river, where he transferred the drive mechanism of the 5 horsepower boiler from the wheels to the paddle wheel and sailed off for the site.

Evans' '*Oruktor Amphibolos*' ('Amphibious Dredge' to you and I) may not have been the world's first car, but it was both the first car in the US and the first amphibious vehicle anywhere on the planet.

11

Guglielmo Marconi & the Radio

For nearly a century scholars and historians have argued about who holds the rightful title of inventor of the radio. Traditionalists tend to come down on the side of Guglielmo Marconi, while others support the claims of Nikola Tesla. The dispute is muddied by the fact that the workings of radio, unlike most of the inventions covered in this book, are bound up in electrical theory, and will therefore prove confusing to readers unfamiliar with the technical jargon of electronics. To keep our own story intelligible we will refrain from references to groundwaves, spark-gap transmitters, coherer-receivers and dipole antennas; rather, we will limit our discussion to who achieved what results when, and why they were given (or not given) credit for their work. Even if you happen to be familiar with this story, we guarantee a few surprises.

As early 19th century experimenters in electricity, Englishmen like Michael Faraday and Humphry Davy had demonstrated that a magnetic field is produced by electrical current. By the middle of the century, Cambridge physics professor James C Maxwell had proved mathematically that electromagnetic fields could be measured at a considerable distance from their source (ie a battery), and that these electrical impulses (or 'waves') moved at the speed of light. It was such mathematical theorizing that laid the groundwork for the invention of radio.

In 1885 and '86 German physics professor Heinrich Hertz actually produced Maxwell's theoretical waves in laboratory experiments. When questioned about his experiments, Hertz admitted that he had no idea to what use these waves might be put: 'It is of no use whatsoever... We just have these mysterious electromagnetic waves that we cannot see... but they are there'.

Science hates the unknown. Only two years after Hertz concluded his experiments, Liverpool University's Oliver (later Sir Oliver) Lodge undertook the first experimental transmission of telegraph messages without the use of wires by carrying the dots and dashes of Morse code via electromagnetic waves. But even Lodge was only conducting experiments for the sake of knowledge; what was needed were individuals willing to take the theoretical science and make it useful in the real world. One of these men was the inventor, physicist and electrical/mechanical wizard, Nikola Tesla.

The world produces very few true geniuses – da Vinci was one, as were Newton and Einstein. So was Nikola Tesla. Not only did Tesla have a photographic memory but he was also able to access his accumulated information, combining it in new and radical ways. Unfortunately for Tesla, these flashes of inspiration were so intense they physically debilitated him – sometimes for hours – but each new idea was clear in the minutest detail. He could dictate precise measurements for every part of a new machine without ever putting pen to paper.

Born in 1856, in what is now Croatia, Tesla should probably have been an Orthodox priest like his father and both grandfathers. Instead, he studied physics and mathematics at Graz Polytechnic and philosophy at Prague University before working as an electrical engineer in Hungary and France.

In 1884, the year before Hertz began his experiments, the nearly penniless Tesla emigrated to the US. Desperate for work, he must have been overjoyed when Thomas Edison offered him a job in his invention factory at Menlo Park, New Jersey.

One of Tesla's early assignments was to redesign Edison's massive Direct Current (DC) generators that powered the Edison Company's electrical grid. According to Tesla, Edison told him that if he could improve their output he would pay him $50,000. It was a shocking amount of money – and work – but within a year Tesla had succeeded. When he asked about the bonus, Edison reportedly told him: 'Tesla, you don't understand our American humour!' Furious, Tesla quit but was rehired by the Westinghouse Electric Corporation, who not only paid him fairly but also allowed him to experiment on his own.

In 1887–88 Tesla took out seven US electrical patents in his own name. When George Westinghouse offered to buy these patents for $60,000 Tesla took the money and set up his own lab in New York City, where he continued his experiments, including work on the wireless transmission of telegraph signals which operated at the same frequency as signals for radio transmission. In 1891 the 35-year-old, newly naturalized American citizen lodged his first patent (number 447920) which dealt with the production of electrical frequencies and would eventually be used in radio transmission. Integral to this was the use of a ground (or earth) wire that allowed for longer transmission ranges.

Already respected for his work, Tesla was frequently invited to lecture on his ideas. A dynamic and engaging speaker, in 1892 and '93 he gave talks and demonstrations on the possibilities of radio wave-based telegraphy at the Franklin Institute in Philadelphia, Pennsylvania, to the National Electric Light Association in St Louis, Missouri and to London's Institute of Electrical Engineers. All of these speeches were widely disseminated in print and translated for reprint in numerous foreign journals. Although Tesla's ideas were new and radical, he explained them so clearly that anyone with technical knowledge could easily understand them and quickly accept them as part of the way of doing things. So it was that Tesla's ideas on radio soon became separated from the man and took on a life of their own. One of the thousands of people who probably read his transcribed lectures was a teenager named Guglielmo Marconi.

Marconi had been born on his father's estate near Bologna, Italy in 1874. The senior Marconi was a wealthy landowner and his mother was one of the heirs to the Irish Jameson Whiskey fortune. It was a good start in life.

Even as a child, Guglielmo had been fascinated by the electrical sciences and read the work of men like Hertz and Maxwell and, no doubt, Tesla. Like many budding inventors, Marconi experimented endlessly with wireless telegraphy. His first experiments, involving equipment based on Oliver Lodge's designs, allowed him to ring a bell in one part of the house via a transmitter in another. Like most early experimenters, Marconi's electrical signals could only travel a few hundred yards before becoming too weak to be received.

In 1895, with an improved antenna, transmitter and receiver of his own devising, Marconi moved his experiments outdoors and found he was able to transmit telegraph messages up to a mile (1.6 km). It was a major accomplishment for such a young man, but a year earlier Oliver Lodge had sent similar signals nearly 20 miles (32 km), and around the same time Tesla, using his new 'Tesla Coil', had spanned a distance of some 50 miles from his New York laboratory up the Hudson river to West Point. Both Lodge and Tesla had already patented their work in the UK and US respectively, and Marconi yearned to exploit his own achievements to the same degree.

With the help of his parents, the 21-year-old Marconi moved to London in 1896 where, thanks to his father's business connections, he met William Preece, Chief Electrical Engineer of the British Post Office who, in turn, arranged for Marconi to demonstrate his wireless telegraphy to government officials. Within the year Marconi was routinely sending signals 8 miles (almost 13 km) across the Bristol Channel.

Thanks to Preece and his father's influential friends – many of whom were Members of Parliament – by July 1897 (four months after receiving a British patent) Marconi had formed the Wireless Telegraph Signal Company which, three years later, became Marconi's Wireless Telegraph Company. To ensure their investment would not be endangered by competition, the powerful forces behind Marconi essentially handed him a government-controlled monopoly on wireless telegraphy, preventing men like Oliver Lodge and others in the British Commonwealth from commercially exploiting their own inventions.

Wisely, Marconi applied for a US patent for equipment which was demonstrably less effective than that already patented – and used – by both Tesla and Lodge. We must assume that Tesla was aware of Marconi's attempts to move into the American market, and in September 1897 he filed for another US patent on improved, long-range transmitting equipment. In this application Tesla stated: 'The apparatus... will... transmit intelligible messages to great distances'.

Two years later, in 1899, Tesla moved his operation from New York to Colorado Springs where, according to what he told reporters, he would attempt to transmit radio signals from nearby Pike's Peak to Paris, 5,600 miles (*c.*9,000 km) away across the Atlantic. Over the next four years Tesla would file for, and be granted, an additional 10 US patents covering his work in radio transmission.

Marconi's inferior market position did nothing to deter him from staking out new business ventures. In 1900 he established Marconi's Wireless Telegraph Company and in the same year set up the Marconi International Marine Communications Company Ltd. In an effort to play 'catch up' with Tesla and Lodge, in 1900 Marconi also filed for, and was granted, British patent number 7777 for an improved, four-circuit transmitter, and quickly filed a patent application in the US; but his work still lagged far behind Tesla's.

Using his improved equipment Marconi engineered a bold manoeuvre designed to assure him pre-eminence in the world of wireless communication. On 12 December 1901 he announced that he had received a radio signal in St John's, Newfoundland which had originated from his station in Cornwall, England – some 2,100 miles (3,379 km) distant. The message he claimed to have received was the single letter 's' sent in Morse code – that is to say, he received three dots. When sceptics in the British Government asked him to repeat the feat in front of witnesses, the greatest distance he could achieve was 700 miles

(1,126 km) – only a third of what he had claimed. The 12 December message may have been nothing more than atmospheric interference.

While Marconi and Tesla were fighting their war of radio waves, the rest of the world was not standing idly by. In 1898, Russian electrical engineer Alexander Popov had established the first ship-to-shore radio transmissions, and two years later he had set up a radio transmitter to communicate from the mainland to the battleship General-Admiral Apraksin. In a speech to the Congress of Russian Electrical Engineers, made in 1900, Popov noted: 'The emission and reception of signals by Marconi... is nothing new... Nikola Tesla carried out the same experiments in 1893.'

While Tesla, Marconi, Lodge and Popov were still busily transmitting Morse code, it was a melon farmer and telephone repairman from Calloway County, Kentucky who seems to have been the first to transmit the human voice over radio waves.

On 1 January 1902, Nathan Stubblefield set up a small radio transmitter and receiver (about 200 feet – 60 m – apart) on the lawn of the local courthouse. The apparatus looked more like two telephones than radio equipment, but these 'phones' were not connected by any wires and the amazed onlookers were able to speak to, and hear, each other clearly. Locally the historic event went unappreciated, but when news of Stubblefield's work reached the *St Louis Post Dispatch* newspaper, a reporter hurried to the Stubblefield farm. There, at a distance of a mile, the astonished reporter conversed with Stubblefield's son and listened to him playing a tune on the harmonica. It was only a matter of weeks before Nathan Stubblefield was called to Washington, DC where he easily established contact between an onshore transmitter and a receiver on the steamship *Bartholdi*.

Curiously, after two more public demonstrations – one in New York and one in Philadelphia – Nathan Stubblefield patented his device but refused to market it. Instead, he simply packed up his radio and went home, never to be heard of again.

But while other enterprising inventors struggled to enter the radio fray, the battle between Marconi and Tesla was heating up.

Marconi's 1900 American patent application, after more than two years of review, was rejected in 1903. In its rejection letter the US Patent Office stated: 'Many of the claims are not patentable over Tesla patent numbers 645,576 and 649,621, of record, the amendment to overcome said references as well as Marconi's pretended ignorance of the nature of a "Tesla Oscillator" being little short of absurd [as] the term Tesla Oscillator has become a household word on both continents [Europe and North America]'.

This rejection seems to have done nothing to dampen Marconi's drive to dominate the world of radio communication. Over the previous three years, stock in the Marconi Wireless Telegraph Company Ltd had risen from a modest $3 per share to $22, and in the US such luminaries as Thomas Edison and Andrew Carnegie invested heavily in Marconi's American company. In Carnegie's case it was just another way to make money; in Edison's it may have been a way of irritating Tesla.

Amazingly, Tesla seemed completely unconcerned by these events. When one of his engineers commented that Marconi seemed to be moving ahead of him, Tesla replied: 'Let him continue. He's using 17 of my patents.' That attitude changed completely in 1904 when, for reasons that have never been fully explained, the US Patent Office struck down Tesla's patents and approved Marconi's. Seven years later, in 1911, to make his position in the market unassailable, Marconi bought out the rights to Oliver Lodge's radio-related patents. But Tesla was finally ready to strike back. In 1915 he filed suit against Marconi for patent infringement and applied for an injunction against the Marconi companies. Sadly, Tesla, who had never been good with money, went into bankruptcy in 1916 and was unable to continue the suit. By 1919 Marconi and his companies held a virtual stranglehold on all wireless communication, in both the US and Great Britain – a position that was quickly reversed in the US when the Government forced him to sell off American Marconi to General Electric.

By the early 1920s both Tesla and Marconi had been effectively sidelined from the rapidly expanding world of radio. Hundreds of independent radio stations were springing up all across America, and in 1922 the BBC (British Broadcasting Corporation) was formed in the UK. Marconi's reputation was not helped when he joined the Italian Fascist Party in 1923 or by his appointment seven years later to the Fascist Grand Council by dictator Benito Mussolini.

If Marconi had made himself unpopular, Tesla had become an object of pity and ridicule. By his middle 60s the years of frustration and overwork had proved too much for his brilliant mind. He developed obsessive-compulsive disorder – causing him to fixate on, and constantly repeat, insignificant actions – and his scientific theories became more and more bizarre. He insisted that time travel, anti-gravity airships and teleportation were all realistic possibilities, and claimed to be in touch with beings from outer space. When Tesla died of heart failure on 5 January 1943 (at the age of 86) he was alone and nearly penniless, despite holding more than 700 patents. Only Thomas Edison ever held more patents, but the majority of these had been developed by men in his employ, including Nikola Tesla.

On 21 June 1943, nearly six months after Tesla's death, the United States Supreme Court reversed the US Patent Office's ruling of 1904, re-establishing all of Tesla's patent rights. Was this a matter of simple justice? Perhaps not. Some years previously, Marconi had lodged a suit against the US Government and the Department of the Army for using radio communications during World War I without paying him the appropriate licence fees. By stripping Marconi of his patents, the Government effectively nullified his lawsuit. The entire affair had been ignominious in the extreme.

What never seems to be mentioned in the story of Tesla, Marconi and the development of radio are the names of Amos Dolbear and Dr Mahlon Loomis. Dolbear, a professor of physics at Tufts College in Boston, Massachusetts had been granted a patent for wireless telegraphy in 1885. For some years Dolbear single-handedly prevented Marconi from establishing a company in the US – at least until Marconi bought out Dolbear's patent rights, just as he would eventually buy out Lodge's.

Mahlon Loomis is quite another story. Dr Loomis was a Washington, DC dentist who claimed to have been experimenting with wireless telegraphy as early as 1862, but who was forced to halt his work when the American Civil War began swirling around the nation's capital. After the war, in 1866, he successfully sent wireless messages between Cohocton Mountain and Beorse Deer Mountain, in Virginia's Blue Ridge range – a distance of 18 miles (29 km). After demonstrating his invention to awe-struck government officials, a bill was introduced into the US Congress attempting to appropriate $50,000 to allow Loomis to develop his system. After two years of inaction, Congress finally permitted Loomis to incorporate the Loomis Aerial Telegraph Company and float $2 million worth of stock. In 1872 President Ulysses S Grant signed the bill into law and Loomis was granted patent number 129,971.

Tragically, Loomis had gone bankrupt during the American economic crisis of 1869 and was unable to exploit the opportunity. Angry, frustrated and broke, Loomis left Washington and moved to the remote village of Terra Alta, West Virginia where he set up a wireless telegraph link between the local railroad station and the town pharmacy – a distance of two miles. Loomis had patented his radio just as the teenage Nikola Tesla was entering university and a full year before Guglielmo Marconi was even born.

12

Orville & Wilbur Wright & the Airplane

From our first awareness that birds could do something we could not, flight became humanity's ultimate dream. As to who first made that dream a reality the answer seems clear. Located beneath a fragile-looking contraption hanging in the Smithsonian Institution's National Air and Space Museum is a brass plaque which proudly proclaims that, on 17 December 1903, brothers Orville and Wilbur Wright became the first men to successfully pilot a power-driven, heavier-than-air flying machine. But is this plaque accurate? To give the Wright brothers their due, they certainly achieved great feats (including, crucially, the invention of the first effective control system), and their tale is remarkable. But as often proves to be the case with history, it is not the whole story.

The Wrights were raised in Dayton, Ohio gy an ecclesiastical family, and although both went to high school, neither completed their education. This was not uncommon in the 19th century when sufficient literacy to read the Bible was generally considered adequate, particularly among rural people. Wilbur completed high school but the family moved before he received his diploma and Orville simply dropped out after completing his junior year. Despite their relative lack of education, the brothers were an enterprising, hard-working pair. Wilbur, born in 1867, was four years older than Orville, and was decidedly the stronger personality of the two. It was his idea to start a local newspaper in 1889 and to shift their efforts to a bicycle shop in 1892. By 1896 the brothers were marketing their own brand of cycle and prospering; but Wilbur was restless and wanted more excitement. Throughout 1898 he scoured local libraries in search of any and all available information on flight. The following year he even wrote to the Smithsonian in Washington, DC asking for additional material on the subject, and began conducting experiments with gliders, going so far as to construct a wind tunnel to measure air currents, wind resistance and 'drag'.

By 1902 the brothers had tested more than 200 different-shaped wing designs, and Wilbur decided they were ready to construct a motorized airplane. Using everything they had learned (including how much power it would take to give the craft 'lift', and how best it could be controlled), they built a light-weight, open-framed biplane whose movements could be controlled by a series of wires and levers that would twist the wing ends to compensate for changes in air currents. The craft had a wingspan of 40 feet (12 m), weighed about 705 pounds (274 kg) without a pilot and was powered by a 12 horsepower (9 kw) engine with a rear-facing propeller to push it through the air.

Having been advised to launch their plane down a hillside (to allow them to build up speed before take-off), fly into a strong headwind (to give them 'lift'), and have a soft place to land, in early December 1903 Orville, Wilbur and the disassembled craft (called the 'Wright Flyer') set off for the Kill Devil Hills sand dunes, a few miles from Kitty Hawk, North Carolina. After waiting out a week of cold driving rain and high winds, the brothers were finally able to make test flights on 17 December. In attendance were men from the local lifeboat station, who helped them drag the Flyer into place, and captured the historic first flight on camera. By the toss of a coin Orville went first. His actual flight lasted about 12 seconds and covered a distance of 120 feet (36 m). That day the brothers carried out three more flights, the best one being the last, in which Wilbur travelled 852 feet (260 m) and reached a height of about 10 feet (3 m); but the Flyer suffered an irreparable crash.

Over the next two years the brothers carried out more than 80 public demonstrations in a new plane, but the press seemed unwilling to believe they were really flying. In 1906 a Paris edition of the *Herald Tribune* went so far as to headline an article 'Flyers or Liars?'; certainly the adverse publicity left both brothers understandably bitter. Still, the question is not whether the Wright brothers flew – they did – but whether they were the first to achieve manned, powered, heavier-than-air flight.

On 18 August 1903 (four months prior to the Wrights' flight) a 30-year-old German civil servant from Hanover named Karl Jatho claimed to have made the first of three flights in a machine he called '*Der Motordrachen*' ('Motor Dragon') in front of four witnesses. Each flight would take place before the Wrights took to the air. On his final flight, in November, Jatho managed to reach a height of 18 feet (almost 6 m) and travel for 200 feet (*c.*60 m). Admittedly, Jatho's controls were so rudimen-tary that he had almost no say over the *Motordrachen*'s direction, but he did achieve powered flight nonetheless.

1903 seems to have been a bumper year for fledgling flyers. While the Wrights and Jatho were doing their thing, so was a 26-year-old New Zealander named Richard Pearse. A farmer from Waitohi on New Zealand's south island, Pearse had always been more interested in mechanical meddling than turning the soil. Sadly for Pearse there had been no money to send him to university, and Waitohi was so isolated that he had no access to libraries. Pearse's experiments had to rely on what information he could glean from magazines. But having so little information freed Pearse from repeating other's mistakes, and led him to create amazingly advanced designs. While everyone else was building bi-planes, Pearse built a single-winged craft. Beneath a framework of linen-covered bamboo Pearse mounted three wheels; a design feature that allowed easier take-off but which would not become standard for more than two decades. He also mounted his propeller facing the front of the plane, rather than the back, and designed what may have been the world's first ailerons to control the plane's movement during flight.

Pearse's first attempts at flight, in 1902, had met with failure due to lack of power, but by the spring of 1903 he had redesigned the engine and was ready to try again. Unlike other early aeronauts, Pearse only told a few close friends what he was doing; he was afraid his provincial-minded neighbours might think he was crazy or a religious heretic. When Pearse finally made his first flight on 31 March 1903 there were few witnesses, but they all later claimed he flew between 150 and 200 feet (45–60 m) before crashing into a hedgerow. Pearse flew again on 2 May, and although the distance was unrecorded, it seems the plane must have reached a height of 15 or more feet (over 4 metres) because that was how far off the ground it was when it again came to rest in a hedgerow. Pearse's third flight, only nine days later, was probably his best and showed just how manoeuverable the craft was. After flying over a 30 foot (*c.*9 m) high river embankment, he made a right turn and followed the river for a distance of nearly 1,000 yards (*c.*900 m) before gliding to a stop on the nearly dry river bed. But Pearse had little ego and never sought publicity. The first newspaper mention of his achievement did not come until six years later when, it seemed, everyone in the world was building planes.

Although Pearse never flew after 1903, in the 1930s he designed, and partially built, a plane that had folding wings (so it could be parked in a standard garage) and had a pivoting engine assembly that hinted at the intriguing possibility of vertical take-off. Given the opportunity, Richard Pearse could have single-handedly revolutionized the aircraft industry.

But even prior to the watershed year of 1903 there were those who yearned for the skies. In 1897 publisher JB Millet asked the Aeronautical Club of Boston, Massachusetts if they could build a flying machine. One club member, 23-year-old Gustave Whitehead, said he thought he could if he had the money. Millet agreed to fund the project and Whitehead set to work. By 1901 he had constructed a sleek monoplane with a bamboo body covered in silk and a 20 horsepower (15 kw) engine that powered two counter-rotating propellers. Revolutionary to the design was a secondary, 10 horsepower (7.5 kw) engine that powered the wheels, thus providing extra speed at take-off. Unlike Pearse, Whitehead was out for all the publicity he could get. When he made his first flight on 14 August 1901, in a field near Fairfield, Connecticut there were reporters from the nearby *Bridgeport Herald* in attendance, the *Boston Transcript* and *New York Herald* reprinting the story later. Tragically, no photographers were present but all three papers duly reported that Whitehead's plane had travelled about 2,500 feet (over 750 m) and reached a height of 45 feet (some 13 m); far better than the Wrights would achieve two years later. Whitehead claimed he took to the air at least one more time, in January 1902, when he purportedly flew 7 miles (*c*.11 kilometres) over Long

Island Sound, but reports are so sketchy that this second flight is almost impossible to confirm.

Another aeronautical contender was Samuel Langley. Langley had always been interested in flight. While teaching physics and astronomy, and directing the Allegheny Observatory in Pittsburgh, Pennsylvania he carried out numerous experiments with scale model aircraft, the first of which actually flew in 1887, the same year he was appointed Secretary of the prestigious Smithsonian Institution. Four years later he published his work and began building larger models. On 6 May 1896, Langley (with the support of the Smithsonian and Alexander Graham Bell) tested a nearly full-sized flying machine known as 'Aerodrome Number 5'. The plane made two unpiloted flights, the most successful carrying it 3,300 feet (over 1,000 m) at a speed of 25 miles per hour (40 km/h). Unfortunately, when Langley scaled up the model to a full-sized vehicle (the 'Great Aerodrome'), and installed Charles Manly as pilot, the craft was simply too heavy to support itself and, according to a government observer who witnessed its test flight in the autumn of that phenomenal year (1903), it 'sank like a lump of concrete'. But Langley had made a significant contribution to American flight, and the Aerodrome went on display in the Smithsonian.

Proper Victorian gentlemen were renowned for dabbling in adventurous pursuits. Because they were 'gentlemen' they obviously had the time and money to indulge their fancies, some of which included flight. Among these was Hiram Maxim, an American who had emigrated to England, made a fortune and was later awarded a knighthood for inventing one of the first fully automated machine guns, in 1885. By the mid-90s Maxim was looking for a new challenge, and decided to build a flying machine – an immense flying machine, powered by steam. Tipping the scales at just over 7,000 pounds (3,175 kg), with a wingspan of 105 feet (32 m) and two steam engines that could produce a combined power of 360 horsepower (268 kw), Maxim's plane was a behemoth. On 31 July 1894 Maxim mounted his craft on 1,800 feet (549 m) of railroad rails, built up a head of steam and released the clutch. Reaching a speed of 42 mph (68 km/h), the craft broke free of the rails and lifted off into space. It only travelled about 200 feet before crashing, but Maxim's steam plane had achieved powered flight. Of course, as you have undoubtedly guessed, it was not the first to do so.

Four years before Maxim's flight a similar achievement had already been accomplished by a French engineer and inventor named Clément Ader. With a string of patents to his name – including several for racing bicycles (*à la* Wright brothers) – Ader's credentials as an inventor were impressive; almost as impressive as the 'Éole', his steam-powered flying machine.

With a boat-shaped body, giant bat-shaped wings, and a revolutionary, lightweight steam engine, the Éole was a properly improbable-looking piece of 19th century engineering. In early October 1890 Ader transported the Éole (named, like Hero's steam turbine, after Aeolus, Greek god of the winds) to the country estate of a friend, outside Paris. While a curious crowd looked on in wonder, Ader chugged along until the Éole lifted from the ground, cruised along for 140 feet (43 m) and crashed. Undaunted, Ader spent the next seven years designing and building an improved plane. Dubbed the 'Avion III' (it was the third generation design) it was larger than the Éole; so large, in fact, that it barely managed to clear the ground. However, according to some reports, it did just that on 14 October 1897, cruising for more than 1,000 feet (some 300 m) before settling back to earth.

Like Ader, fellow Frenchman and naval officer Félix du Temple de la Croix (commonly known as Félix du Temple) liked experimenting with things that flew; and he did so more than a decade before Ader. Du Temple's first patent for a flying machine was granted in 1857, but none of his full-sized machines actually took to the air until 1874. Even by the standards of half a century later, du Temple's achievement was ground-breaking in many ways, not the least of which was a retractable landing gear that reduced 'drag' when the vehicle was in flight.

If more than 16 years of experiments taught du Temple anything it was that the small, portable steam engines of his time did not produce enough power to lift a plane into the air. So he designed one that would. Small, lightweight and with a rapidly circulating water system, du Temple's engine was nothing short of revolutionary. His plane was no less astounding. With an aluminium frame and a single-wing design, it was sleek, fast and weighed only 160 pounds (73 kg) without the pilot. After several trial runs du Temple managed to achieve lift-off by sliding the plane down a hillside. Not only did the plane fly (if briefly), but it returned safely to the ground, making du Temple the first man to successfully break the bonds of gravity in a manned, powered, heavier-than-air craft. The Wright brothers would use a similar take-off method and, on their first flight, travel a slightly shorter distance; but it would be another 29 years before they did so.

Du Temple may never have improved on his flying machine, but the lightweight, high-pressure steam engine he designed to power it made him a fortune. His amazing plane was put on display at the 1878 World Fair in Paris as testimony to his historic flight.

There is one other team of aviation pioneers who deserve a mention. In the rural English county of Somerset, during the 1830s and '40s, John Stringfellow busied himself manufacturing machine parts for the lace-making industry. But Stringfellow's goals were a lot bigger. In 1843 he and William Henson launched the Aerial Transit Company with the intention of hauling people all over the world in the steam-powered aircraft they insisted they could build. Their publicity was impressive; posters and fliers showing their steam-powered plane puffing its way high above the Pyramids of Egypt and the Taj Mahal in India. Throughout the 1840s they experimented with scale models and, in 1848 (Henson having emigrated to America), inside a cavernous, abandoned factory in the local town of Chard, Stringfellow managed to successfully launch a 10 foot (3 m) wingspan, steam-powered scale model into the air. The model flew under its own power (its flight path guided by a wire) for about 10 feet before coming to rest. The full-sized plane, with its proposed wingspan of 150 feet (46 m) and a weight of 3,000 pounds (*c.*1,300 kg), never got off the ground, but the model was placed on display at London's Crystal Palace in 1868. The planes may have been unmanned, but Stringfellow and Henson were the first to prove that powered flight was possible.

Discounting Stringfellow and Henson, who only flew models, and Langley, we have looked at a total of six men who successfully built and flew manned, powered, heavier-than-air craft before Orville and Wilbur ever got their feet off the ground. So why do the Wrights get the credit? There is of course the vital issue of control, but, again, there is more to the tale than this.

Although Samuel Langley died in 1906, his Aerodrome remained on display at the Smithsonian and was touted as being the first heavier-than-air craft 'capable' of manned, powered flight – which it obviously was not. Still, the Smithsonian, as the keeper of all things American, wanted to display the Wright Flyer in their collection, but relegate it to a place of less significance than Langley's craft. By the early 1920s the Smithsonian were chasing Orville (Wilbur having died in 1912) for the rights to the Flyer, which had lain in pieces since it crashed in 1903. Refusing to take second place to Langley's accomplishment, in 1928 Orville rebuilt the Flyer and loaned it to the London Science Museum. Although such notables as American aviator Charles Lindbergh tried to arbitrate the dispute, Orville remained adamant, and the Flyer remained in exile in England.

Orville passed away in January 1948 and, finding his heirs as hard-headed as he had been, by November of that year the Smithsonian finally gave in. Langley's plane was removed from display and on 17 December 1948, 45 years to the day after it flew, the Wright Flyer was given pride of place in the Smithsonian's main rotunda. Beneath the plane was a plaque proclaiming that Orville and Wilbur Wright had been the first men to achieve manned, powered, heavier-than-air flight. According to the terms of the agreement between the Smithsonian and the Wright family, should the museum ever admit to any alternative possibility, the plane would be returned to the Wright family. To this day, if you ask the Smithsonian who first achieved this feat, they will likely point to the plaque and say 'the Wright brothers'.

13

Henry Ford, Mass Production & the Assembly Line

Henry Ford and the story of his rise to fame and fortune, thanks largely to the success of the 'Model T', has grown to such gargantuan proportions that most people are no longer sure exactly why Ford became famous in the first place.

In Chapter 10 we dismissed the legend that Ford invented the automobile. There are those who believe he built the first car in America, but automotive historians generally credit that feat to Charles and Frank Duryea, in 1893. In fact, the first American car was built two years earlier by John Lambert in Ohio City. What the Duryea brothers did was establish the first automobile factory in the US, in 1895, thus discounting yet another possible claim about Ford. The most commonly accepted belief about Ford is that he was the first man to produce cars on an assembly line, thus allowing him to build them faster and cheaper. Wrong again. The first automotive assembly line was established by Ransom Olds, in 1901, for the production of his 'curved dash' Oldsmobile – and he achieved some success with the process. In his first year

(1901) Olds produced 425 cars, but by 1902 he was spitting them out at a rate of 2,500 per annum.

Before we return to Henry Ford and his part in this story we should pause for a moment to explore exactly what an assembly line is. The assembly line, above all else, is the apex of the industrialization process. The object being manufactured is moved from man to man; each worker adding one or more parts to the product until it is complete. Integral to this process are interchangeable parts. If the assembly line is to work efficiently, the worker must be able to randomly pick a part, or parts, from a bin and add them to the item being produced without having to file or shape them so they fit into place. This process not only provides for speedy manufacture but also allows for easy replacement of any part that might eventually break. This is the process that Olds first used in automotive manufacturing and which Ford applied so successfully that his name has become inextricably linked with it. But why is Ford remembered over Olds?

Born in 1863 on the family farm in Michigan, Henry Ford was apprenticed out to a machinist in Detroit at the age of 16. By the time he was 28 he was working as an engineer at the Detroit offices of the Edison Illuminating Company. It was a respectable, well-paying job and gave Henry enough money to indulge his interest in mechanics. In 1896, only five years after going to work for Edison, Ford built his first automobile, a spindly-looking four-wheeled buggy powered by an internal combustion engine he had constructed himself. Taking what must have seemed like an insane risk, Ford quit his job three years later, going on to found the Ford Motor Company with the proclamation 'I will build a motor car for the great multitude'. Unfortunately, his first cars were anything but. Hand-crafted cars are immensely expensive things and Ford's market was therefore limited to the rich, and even at this early period there were already 30 auto manufacturers competing for the high-end market. If Ford was going to survive in the business he had to offer something the competition could not.

By 1908, only five years after going into business, Ford had limited his production to one model – the 'T' – its name indicating that it was the 20th design he had come up with (though not all designs had been produced). That year, with 125 employees working in small groups, assembling each car from start to finish, the price of a Model T was $825. Still too costly to reach anything like a mass market, but Ford managed to sell a record-setting 10,000 vehicles. Insisting that he would not build a car that his workers could not afford to buy, Ford and his general manager began to devise ways of speeding up production and lowering costs.

Within the year the Ford plant had been rearranged. Engines and major parts were assembled on the top floor and then sent down through the two lower floors, where the car was slowly put together. By the time the assemblage reached the ground floor, the frame and chassis were pulled along on ropes, with pieces of the body being added at designated stations on the factory floor. Each man carried out only a single task, like setting the engine in place or installing the pre-made seats. Individual craftsmanship may have been lost, but assembly time dropped significantly.

It took Ford and his foremen five years to perfect the assembly line, but by August 1913 production of the Model T was entirely automated. The workers no longer went to the car, the car came to the workers. The undercarriage of the car rolled along on a continuously moving belt and part after part was added to the frame until the completed car rolled out the door of the plant. Thanks to a mechanized assembly line, Ford reduced the price of the Model T to $390 and sold more cars than all of his competitors put together – a staggering 248,000.

Mass-produced, interchangeable parts and an automated assembly line may have put America (as well as Britain and Canada) on wheels, but even Henry Ford admitted the factory system was not his idea. To quote Ford: 'The idea came to me, in a general way, from the overhead trolleys that the Chicago meat-packers use in dressing beef.' In the vast slaughterhouses of Chicago, cattle carcasses were hung upside down and the butchers carved away one cut at a time until there was nothing left. All Ford did was reverse the process, adding parts to the skeleton of his cars until they were complete. But where did the meat-packers get the idea from?

The Waltham Watch Company of Waltham, Massachusetts used an identical system, with a moving conveyor belt and men adding specific parts to watches, as early as 1888. Thirty years before, in 1858, Oliver Winchester had used a similar method (minus the conveyor belt) in the assembly of .22 calibre rifles, at his plant in New Haven, Connecticut. Winchester had undoubtedly adopted the system from the Springfield Armory, a United States government arsenal located in Springfield, Massachusetts where military muskets were being successfully manufactured with inter-changeable parts as early as 1825. Even at this early date the process of using mass-produced, interchangeable parts was becoming known among the British and Europeans as the 'American' system of manufacturing. But was the system really American, and did the gun and watch-makers develop it?

Henry Maudslay, like his father before him, worked at London's Woolwich Arsenal, but by 1797 Henry had left the Arsenal and set up in business as a manufacturer of the wooden pulleys used to rig sailing ships. The pulleys, or block-and-tackle, were fairly simple – two wooden side plates and two or more axle-mounted, wooden wheels through which the rope rigging was run. To manufacture the pulley parts more efficiently, Maudslay worked with his friends Samuel Bentham and French-born engineer Marc Isambard Brunel (father of Isambard Kingdom Brunel) to design lathes that would automatically turn identical pulley wheels. More machines sawed the side plates, drilled holes in appropriate locations and so on. With the parts mass produced by machine, the blocks could be assembled by virtually unskilled labour.

These inexpensive rigging blocks may have been revolutionary but the idea of sub-dividing labour to speed up production had been suggested as early as 1776, by economist Adam Smith, in his book *The Wealth of Nations*; Maudslay and Brunel had only put it into practice.

Thanks to Smith's book, and the economic revolution it espoused, the idea of mass production and the division of labour spread like wildfire to every place concerned with more efficient ways of manufacturing. One such place was the newly independent United States. Long on ambition but short on manpower, the US was always ready to listen to someone with new ideas. One such person was Eli Whitney.

Born in Westborough, Massachusetts in 1765, Whitney had lots of clever ideas, but very little cash. He yearned to go to college, but his family had not saved the necessary money, so Eli (short for Elias) spent his late teens and early 20s as an apprentice blacksmith. Here, his natural mechanical aptitude showed itself when he designed a nail-making machine – a vast improvement over forging them by hand. Whitney, it would seem, was as bright as he was clever, and when he finally graduated from Yale in 1792 he was '*Phi Beta Kappa*', the highest undergraduate honour possible in an American university.

After graduation, Whitney visited friends in the South where he observed plantation slaves labouring days on end picking the tiny seeds from cotton boles. It could easily take a slave an entire day to clean a single pound of cotton fibre – a system so time consuming that cotton growing was only marginally profitable. In a matter of 10 days Whitney had devised a prototype machine that could clean a pound of cotton in a matter of minutes. The following year (1793) Whitney returned north and established a firm to manufacture his Cotton Engine, or 'Cotton Gin'. His production methods were almost identical to those used four years later by Henry Maudslay. The wooden parts for the gin were mass produced by specialized machines and assembled by unskilled, or semi-skilled, labourers.

Being a clever and resourceful fellow, Whitney now sought a new outlet for his manufacturing know-how, and it was the French who provided it.

In 1798 the French, under Napoleon Bonaparte, were making war on everyone within reach, and the arms shipments which the US Government had formerly purchased from England and France dried up as Europe and Britain prepared for war. The US Federal Government had established an armoury at Springfield, Massachusetts four years earlier, but by 1799 it had only produced 7,750 muskets; hardly enough to make up the shortfall.

Although he had no experience in gun-smithing, Whitney managed to get an appointment with President John Adams by insisting he could provide vast amounts of weapons in an astoundingly short period of time, as a result of the new process of manufacturing he had devised. It was probably thanks to fellow Yale alumni, Secretary of the Treasury Oliver Wolcott, that

Whitney was granted the audience. Whitney had written to Wolcott on 13 May 1798 saying: 'I am persuaded that Machinery moved by water adapted to this Business would greatly diminish the labor and facilitate the manufacture of this Article'.

On 14 June 1798 Whitney walked away with a contract to manufacture 10,000 muskets over the next 28 months for the sum of $134,000. All he had to do now was build a factory, design and build the necessary machinery and hire and train the workers.

Not surprisingly, more than a year passed without a single musket showing up. In July 1799 Whitney explained the delay to Wolcott by describing his concept in detail: 'One of my primary objectives is to form the tools so that the tools themselves shall fashion the work and give to every part its just proportion, which when once accomplished, will give expedition, uniformity and exactness to the whole.'

There is no doubt that Whitney was making progress in setting up the world's first automated, mass-production plant. He designed one machine after another to carry out the dozens of individual processes necessary to manufacture musket components; but when another year and a half went by without a single gun being delivered to Washington, Whitney was called to the capital to explain himself.

When he met with President Adams, President-elect Thomas Jefferson and members of the Cabinet and War Department, Whitney had a little demonstration ready for them. Laid out on a row of tables were piles of every part necessary to build a dozen or more muskets; Whitney then challenged the founding fathers of his country to pick any part, fit it to any adjoining part and so on until they had assembled a complete musket, assuring them that all the parts were interchangeable. Later, Jefferson wrote to his friend, James Monroe: 'He has invented moulds and machines for making all the pieces of his lock so exactly equal that [you can] take [the] locks to pieces and mingle their parts and a hundred locks may be put together... by taking the first pieces which come to hand.'

Whitney got the time extension he requested and finally delivered the last of the 10,000 muskets in 1809, more than 10 years after signing the contract, and nearly eight years later than stipulated. As impressive as his demonstration may have seemed, it is just possible that it was a stitch-up. More than a century after his death a number of Whitney muskets were disassembled and it was found that the parts were not inter-changeable after all. Still, he had the right idea, and had convinced his government it would work. More to our point, however, is that while Jefferson described Whitney's demonstration in glowing terms, it was probably all old news to him.

Benjamin Franklin (who was not only a close friend of Jefferson but a fellow inventor and technologist) had served as America's ambassador to France between 1776 and 1785. While there, Franklin wrote to Jefferson describing a musket workshop operated by a man named Le Blanc where, it would seem, the gun parts were mass produced and completely interchangeable. Later, from 1785 until 1789, Jefferson replaced Franklin as America's ambassador to France and went to visit Le Blanc's workshop to witness this marvel of technology first hand. We know that Jefferson was there because he described his visit in a letter to John Jay, first Chief Justice of the US Supreme Court. We also know that in either 1800 or 1801 a 'foreign pamphlet on arms manufacturing techniques' was sent to Eli Whitney by his old friend, US Treasury Secretary Oliver Wolcott. Jefferson himself discussed Le Blanc's process with Whitney only eight months prior to the delivery of Whitney's first shipment of muskets to the Federal Government.

It would seem that Le Blanc had used the ploy of demonstrating his process by displaying piles of random parts before a group of French government ministers and military men, and challenging them to build their own guns. It had worked once, in France, so surely, Whitney reasoned, it would work again in the States. Unlike the Americans, however, the French were ultimately not impressed. The highly skilled French craftsmen who traditionally built guns were horrified that they might be driven out of business by this new method, and Le Blanc's process was scrapped.

But even Le Blanc, pioneer that he was, was not the first to use mass-produced, interchangeable parts and an assembly line. Between 1699 and the mid-1740s, Swedish mining engineer and inventor Christopher Polhem used this same system to manufacture inexpensive clocks in his factory at Stjärnsund, Sweden.

Sadly, like their French counterparts, Swedish craftsmen feared they would be put out of work by Polhem's cheap clocks and the system was never widely adopted.

To find an instance where the early mass production of parts and bulk manufacturing of goods was met not with scepticism but enthusiasm we need to travel 250 years further back in time to the year 1450. That year, in the town of Mainz, Germany a goldsmith named Johannes Gutenberg first used movable type to print manuscripts. As a skilled craftsman, Gutenberg would have known how to cut the moulds from which an almost limitless number of identical metal letters could be cast. The only skills the typesetter would need were the ability to spell and to arrange the type backwards in the tray so the printed page came out the right way round. The printing process itself took only minimal training, and once a page of type had been set and put on the bed of the press, an almost endless production run of pages could be set in motion. The process was not complicated, and one printing press could turn out books and pamphlets far faster than 100 monks copying manuscripts by hand.

But even Gutenberg probably 'borrowed' the idea. The first known use of interchangeable, cast-metal type used in conjunction with a printing press took place in Korea around the year 1230, and was originated by a man named Chae Yun-eui. Considering the number of adventurers, traders and missionaries that travelled from Europe to the Orient between 1230 and 1450 it is unlikely that an educated man like Gutenberg would not have encountered at least one printed book before he figured out how they were made. This first Korean printing press was a success for the same reason the device would become a success in Europe more than two centuries later, and offered precisely the same advantage it would give Henry Ford almost seven centuries later – automation produced more units of a commodity, and did so at less cost per unit, than doing the same job by hand.

So why is Henry Ford still thought of as the man who brought the world into the age of mass production? A look at statistics from the Ford Motor Company archives may provide the answer. When Ford succeeded in automating his production line in 1913 it took about 10 hours to build a Model T, and that year he sold 248,000 cars at $550 each. The next year he dropped the price and upped production, giving Ford an unprecedented 48% share of the US automotive market. By the time the little black car that put America on wheels ceased production in late 1927, a Model T was rolling off the production line every 24 seconds and the price stood at a modest $250.

Over the 19 years of its production, more than 15 million Model T Fords rolled off the line! It was an automotive production record that would only ever be surpassed by the Volkswagen 'Beetle', but it took Volkswagen some 30 years to do what Ford had done in a mere 19.

Henry Ford may not have invented mass production, interchangeable parts or the production line, but what he did with them would be pretty hard to top.

14

James Watson, Francis Crick & the Discovery of DNA

Since the mid-1950s James Watson and Francis Crick have been two of the best known names in modern science. Indeed, in 1962 they (along with Maurice Wilkins) were awarded the Nobel Prize for their identification of DNA as the primary carrier of genetic information. But were Watson and Crick solely responsible for its discovery?

Deoxyribonucleic acid, commonly known as DNA, is the material buried deep in the nucleus of every cell in every living organism on the planet which determines why a particular life form possesses particular characteristics. DNA makes sure that cats have fur, elephants have trunks and that oak trees bear oak leaves; it also determines why our hair, eyes and skin are one particular colour rather than another. In human beings each cell contains 23 pairs of chromosomes, and the DNA in these chromosomes combines in an almost infinite number of combinations to guarantee that each of us is an individual, distinct from the other six billion people on the planet.

The first systematic exploration of genetics took place during the 1860s when an Austrian monk named Gregor Mendel determined that he could accurately predict the colour of pea blossoms by cross-breeding peas with flowers of different colours. The significance of Mendel's discovery was not properly understood until the third decade of the 20th century, but by then scientists understood that the genetic information in every life form was hidden somewhere in the tangle of acids and proteins inside the nucleus of each cell. In 1935 Professor Erwin Chargaff of Columbia University published a ground-breaking paper detailing several of these nucleic acids (acids contained in the nucleus of a cell), including DNA. One of Chargaff's hypotheses was that the make-up of DNA differs in every plant and animal species, thus marking it as individual from all others. Chargaff's work was supported in 1944 by an American scientist named Oswald Avery, who believed that DNA alone determined the physical characteristics of all living things.

While the work of Chargaff and Avery has since proven correct, at the time most scientists believed it was the protein in the heart of the cell, not the DNA, which carried genetic information. Although incorrect, this was not an unreasonable assumption. Cell nuclei contain a lot more protein than DNA, and that protein is packed full of chains of complex chemicals; just the sort of place genetic information could easily be stored.

One of the most respected individuals working on the genetic puzzle during this period was Dr Linus

Pauling. A professor at the California Institute of Technology (CalTech), Pauling was both a quantum chemist and biochemist of the highest order. Thanks to his cutting edge work in X-ray diffraction he became a leading name in the field now known as molecular biology. In 1948 Pauling, who was one of those convinced that the genetic code was linked to proteins, discovered that many proteins exist in the shape of a helix – or spiral. By 1951 Pauling had authored hundreds of papers and several prominent textbooks on chemistry in general and cell structure in particular, was recognized as the world's leading structural chemist, and had been elevated to the head of CalTech's Chemistry Department. Still, he firmly believed that the genetic code was linked to proteins, not DNA, because, as he put it: 'I was so pleased with proteins... that I thought [they] probably are the hereditary material rather than nucleic acids.'

At this time, Pauling's only serious competitor for discovering the hiding place of the genetic blueprint was Sir Lawrence Bragg. Already a Nobel Prize winner, and head of the Cavendish Laboratories at Cambridge University, Bragg and Pauling had been in gentlemanly competition since the late 1920s – but Bragg, too, was convinced that the secret lay in proteins, not DNA.

Also in 1951, while Pauling and Bragg worked on their separate projects, a scientific team at King's College, London was doing similar work. This team, headed by Professor Maurice Wilkins, a member of the Medical Research Council Biophysics Unit, had been experimenting with DNA and other nucleic acids using the relatively new technique of X-ray crystallography, a technique which had been championed by Linus Pauling. In January 1951, Wilkins (who had been looking for a new assistant knowledgeable in X-ray crystallography) was away on holiday when a candidate was finally selected by his superiors at King's College. Her name was Dr Rosalind Franklin. Franklin had been working with X-ray crystallography since 1947 and was experienced in taking X-rays of DNA structure. Because Wilkins had been busy on other projects for several months, and done no work on DNA, the entire project was handed over to Franklin. It was an inadvertent move that would forever taint Wilkins' relationship with his new colleague.

Rosalind Franklin was absolutely dedicated to the scientific method. She moved cautiously, slowly and carefully, never assuming anything and verifying every finding before she even considered announcing, or publishing, her work. As a result, many of her co-workers, including Wilkins, considered her aloof and cold, if not downright secretive. There was no doubt, however, that she got results. By mid-summer 1951 Franklin had produced the best X-ray pictures of DNA that had ever been taken. Dutifully, she shared these with Wilkins. When Linus Pauling learned about the DNA X-rays he wrote to King's requesting copies of them, but was refused.

Later that year, while Wilkins and Franklin were busy with their work, and Pauling remained temporarily stymied, Sir Lawrence Bragg and the Cavendish Laboratories at Cambridge took on a new team member. Dr James Watson was only 23 years old but he had already earned a PhD in zoology in his native United States before coming to England to do post-doctoral work. Watson, who had a consuming interest in biochemistry and genetics, had originally wanted to earn his doctoral degree at CalTech, where Pauling taught, but had been unable to gain admittance. This did nothing to deter his interest and he felt immediately at home at the Cavendish Labs, becoming close friends with his office partner, Francis Crick, a 35-year-old British graduate student and PhD candidate with a background in physics, molecular biology and neuroscience.

Although neither Watson nor Crick was assigned to work on any aspect of the sticky problem of the genetic code, it was one of many interests which they had in common. Unlike most of their more experienced contemporaries, including Dr Bragg, their superior, and Dr Linus Pauling, both Watson and Crick leaned toward the more radical opinion that the genetic code lay in DNA rather than protein. While they were both certainly bright enough to understand the basics of Pauling's work, neither of them had sufficient background in chemistry to carry out the experiments that would have been necessary to prove their hypothesis and trump both Pauling and their boss. In fact, of the six major players in the race to pinpoint the genetic code – Pauling, Bragg, Wilkins, Franklin,

Watson and Crick – only Linus Pauling and Rosalind Franklin held advanced degrees in chemistry.

While the other four followed their own paths toward proving their personal beliefs in the genetic resting place, Watson and Crick decided to follow Sherlock Holmes' advice and arrive at the correct answer by simple deductive reasoning. As Watson put it, they would 'imitate Pauling and beat him at his own game'.

In November 1951, word reached the Cavendish Laboratories that Rosalind Franklin was going to deliver a departmental seminar at King's College. Watson realized this could be an important source of information if he and Crick wanted to make themselves serious contenders in the DNA race. Although Watson attended the lecture we have found no record that he took notes, and when he reported back to Crick, his recollections of the talk were sketchy; Franklin's descriptions of X-ray crystallography were outside his area of knowledge. What he was clear about, however, was that he was unimpressed with Franklin's ability to explain her ideas clearly and hold her audience's attention. Simply put, Watson thought Franklin a complete bore.

Based on what he could remember, Watson together with Crick assembled a physical model of what they assumed DNA must look like. In simple terms, their model was a triple helix and looked not unlike a three-strand rope-twist. Excited by what they had accomplished, Watson and Crick invited Franklin and her superior, Maurice Wilkins, to Cambridge to see their model. The meeting did not go well. Wilkins was obviously distressed that they had undertaken such work because an unwritten agreement existed between Cambridge and King's College that only the scientists at King's would work on DNA; those at Cambridge would concentrate on proteins. Franklin was more pointed in her criticism. She told them in no uncertain terms that their model was utterly wrong. Despite Watson and Crick's efforts to convince Wilkins and Franklin to co-operate with them in developing another, more accurate model of DNA, the King's College team left Cambridge feeling bitter. Embarrassed by the whole affair, Bragg flatly forbade Watson and Crick to work on DNA.

At almost the same time the Cambridge fiasco was taking place, Linus Pauling was applying for a passport to visit England, where he was to be guest of honour at a special meeting of the Royal Society, slated to discuss the question of nucleic proteins. As the meeting was scheduled to take place on 1 May 1952, he should have had plenty of time to renew his passport. In those dark days of America's anti-communist witch-hunt, how-ever, anyone like Linus Pauling who spoke out against nuclear weapons was labelled anti-American. The State Department refused to grant the passport, and only after a massive outcry from the scientific community was it grudgingly issued – but by the time Pauling arrived in the UK the conference had been over for 10 weeks. Still, Pauling visited most of the people he would have seen at the Royal Society – most, that is, except Maurice Wilkins and his team at King's College. Had he done so he might have seen Rosalind Franklin's X-ray photographs of DNA, and those images might have caused him to change the course of his investigations from protein to DNA. But Pauling had asked for copies of Franklin's X-ray photos nearly a year earlier and been refused, would he now have been allowed access to them? We will probably never know.

If Pauling remained unaware of the importance of Franklin's work, the atmosphere in Franklin's own lab was deteriorating to the point of universal frustration. Throughout 1952 Franklin continued her experiments, calculating and recalculating, checking and rechecking every detail and refusing to discuss her work with anyone until she was satisfied. Having virtually no idea where she was in this process, Wilkins tried to reproduce her work but was unable to achieve the same quality of X-rays that Franklin continually turned out.

Meanwhile, at Cambridge, Watson and Crick tried to rethink their model of DNA but lacked the necessary information to progress beyond their original three-twist concept. They must have been delighted therefore when, with the autumn term, a new graduate student arrived to work with them. His name was Peter Pauling, son of none other than Linus Pauling. Through general chit-chat Crick and Watson were able to keep themselves abreast of what progress the senior Pauling was making and, in turn, Peter Pauling kept his father informed about what Watson and Crick were up to. In January of 1953 Peter Pauling announced that his father had sent him a draft copy of a paper describing what he believed to be the true structure of DNA. To Watson and Crick's amazement, the structure described in Pauling's paper was nearly identical to their own all-too-flawed three-twist model of the previous year.

Frantic that they had been co-opted, but certain that if they had been wrong then so too was Pauling, Watson took a copy of the paper to King's and showed it to Rosalind Franklin. In her usual unsubtle manner, Franklin discounted Pauling's findings as complete garbage and abruptly dismissed Watson from her laboratory. Angry and hurt, Watson went off to find Maurice Wilkins. Already frustrated with Franklin's plodding and secretive nature, Wilkins showed Watson copies of Franklin's latest – and by far best – X-ray photos of DNA, without first asking her permission; it was an unconscionable breach of trust and etiquette.

Returning to Cambridge, Watson immediately told his boss that both Franklin and Wilkins had confirmed that Pauling was on the wrong track. Seeing that his old scientific competitor was so far off the mark, Bragg allowed Watson and Crick to resume their attempts to build a model of DNA. Of course, what Bragg could not know was that, having seen Franklin's X-rays, Watson now knew what DNA actually looked like and had a general idea of how to interpret it in physical form.

Excitedly, Watson discussed his new information with Crick and described his new understanding of how DNA actually differed from their original model. It was not a triple helix, but a simple double helix – much like a twisted step-ladder.

Both Watson and Crick were familiar with the work of Erwin Chargaff, and knew that their idea of how DNA should look could only be confirmed if it fitted what are known as 'Chargaff's Rules'. To avoid another debacle like the one they had experienced during their first attempt at a model, Crick had met up with Chargaff. Recalling the meeting later, in 1978, Chargaff stated: 'So far as I could make out, they wanted, unencumbered by any knowledge of the chemistry involved, to fit DNA into a helix... they did not seem to know much about anything...' Still, on 28 February 1953, Crick rushed to the Eagle pub in Cambridge where he found Watson and some colleagues enjoying a drink. Barely containing his excitement, Crick announced, according to Watson's own recollection: 'We have found the secret of life!'

Over the ensuing weeks Watson and Crick worked to assemble a physical representation of DNA that would fit both Franklin's X-rays, Chargaff's Rules and their own theories. When the information they had did not work, or they hit a stumbling block, they consulted with Maurice Wilkins who nudged them back toward the correct path. Unlike Franklin, Crick and Watson were natural collaborators, using each other as sounding-boards and making key connections.

As winter turned to spring, Crick and Watson prepared to release word of their work. Courteously, they asked Maurice Wilkins if he wanted to collaborate on the paper they were readying for publication but, for reasons that can only be imagined, he turned them down. Some time in early mid-March, Wilkins learned that Franklin was finally content enough with her work that she, too, was preparing a paper for publication. Quickly, so as not to be left out, Wilkins wrote to Crick asking if he and Watson would mind if he, Wilkins, worked up his own paper for simultaneous publication. Crick and Watson expressed no objections. It must have been an amazed scientific community that picked up the April 1953 edition of *Nature* magazine to find not one, not two, but three papers on the true nature and significance of DNA. Amazingly, Watson and Crick's piece, entitled 'Molecular Structure of Nucleic Acids – A Structure for Deoxyribose Nucleic Acid', was so short that it is what scientists refer to not as an article but a letter.

While describing their model in some detail ('suggesting' to the wider world what is now accepted as the first accurate model of DNA structure), they offered scant historical background to their work or reference to authorities on whose work they had based their particular two helical chain model. The only acknowledgement they offered King's was: 'We have also been stimulated by a knowledge of the general nature of the unpublished experimental results and ideas of Dr MHF Wilkins, Dr RE Franklin, and their co-workers at King's College, London.'

Only days after Watson and Crick submitted their article to *Nature*, but prior to its publication, Linus Pauling arrived in Cambridge. By this time he fully realized that he had spent years following a dead end in his search for the genetic blueprint of life, and that the true genetic determinant was not protein but DNA. When he was taken to see Watson and Crick's model, Pauling conceded that this was undoubtedly the true structure of DNA. Watson himself remembered Pauling's concession as having been given with gentlemanly good grace.

Long before they were awarded the 1962 Nobel Prize, Watson and Crick had become the most famous names in bio-science. Sadly, Rosalind Franklin died of cancer at the age of 37 in 1958 and, as a Nobel Prize cannot be awarded posthumously, she was not included in the list of candidates. Her old colleague, who had shown her work without her knowledge, Maurice Wilkins, was on the list and, ultimately, shared the prize with Watson and Crick. In Watson and Crick's Nobel lectures they cited 98 learned references, but none of them included the name of Rosalind Franklin. Only Wilkins mentioned her at all, and then only to say 'Rosalind Franklin made some very valuable contributions to the X-ray analysis.'

Linus Pauling was not recognized for his work in genetics, but that same year he did receive the Nobel Peace Prize for his stand against above-ground nuclear testing. This was in fact his second Nobel Prize (the first received for Chemistry in 1954), making him the only man in history to win two, unshared Nobel Prizes.

Rosalind Franklin has never received the recognition she deserved. In a 1977 interview, Ava Pauling, wife of Linus Pauling, remarked: '[If] ever there was a woman who was mistreated it was Rosalind Franklin, and she didn't get the notice that she should have gotten for her work on DNA.' Still, time is slowly redressing the balance. In 2003 the Royal Society established the Rosalind Franklin Award for an outstanding contribution to any area of natural science, engineering or technology.

Key Sources

1 Christopher Columbus & the Discovery of America

Bailey, J, *Sailing to Paradise – The discovery of the Americas by 7000 BC* (Simon & Schuster: 1995)

Bischoff, B, *Latin Palaeography – Antiquity & the Middle Ages* (Cambridge University Press: 1990)

Clement, RW, 'Italian Sixteenth-Century Writing Books and the Scribal Reality of Verona', *Visible Language*, volume 20, 1986

Forbes, JD, *The American Discovery of Europe* (University of Illinois Press: 2007)

Herodotus (Godley, AD, trans), *The Histories I–IV* (Harvard University Press: 1963)

Lisboa, LC and Andrade, RP, *Great Enigmas of Mankind* (Círculo do Livro Press: 1969) – Chapter 5, Columbus' Antecessors

Warmington, BH, *Carthage* (Robert Hale, 2nd edition: 1969)

Washburn, W, 'Exploration and Discovery before 1492', *The Christopher Columbus Encyclopedia*, volume 1, 1992

Williams, GA, *Madoc – The making of a myth* (Oxford University Press: 1987)

Williams, T, *The Forgotten People* (Gomer Press: 1996)

www.brasilemb.org
www.cristobalcolondeibiza.com
www.lewrockwell.com
www.muweb.millersville.edu
www.northvegr.org
www.phoenicia.org
www.press.uillinois.edu
www.sacred-texts.com
www.sevenoceans.com
www.welshdragon.net
www.wsu.edu

2 James Watt & the Steam Engine

Acta Eruditorum (Leipzig: 1698)

Hart, R, 'Reminiscences of James Watt', Transactions of the Glasgow Archaeological Society, 1859

Inventions of the Ancients – Hero of Alexandria (Macdonald: 1971) – facsimile of the 1851 Woodcroft edition

Papin, D, *Les Nouvelles Expériences du Vuide, avec la Description des Machines qui Servent à les Faire* (Paris: 1674)

Savery, T, *The Miner's Friend – Or, an engine to raise water by fire* (1702)

Smeaton, J, *Reports of the late John Smeaton FRS*, volume 1, 1798

www.acmi.net.au
www.campus.udayton.edu
www.dimdima.com
www-groups.dcs.st-and.ac.uk
www.history.rochester.edu
www.homepages.tscnet.com
www.iihr.uiowa.edu
www.inventors.about.com
www.library.thinkquest.org
www.sjsu.edu
www.tmth.edu.gr

3 Samuel Morse & the Telegraph

Bowers, B, *Sir Charles Wheatstone FRS, 1802–1875* (HMSO: 1975)

Bunch, B and Hellemans, A, *The Timetables of Technology – A chronology of the most important people and events in the history of technology* (Simon & Schuster: 1993)

Chandler, AD (ed) and Cortada, JW (ed), *A Nation Transformed by Information – How information has shaped the United States from colonial times to the present* (Oxford University Press: 2000)

Johnson, P, *The Birth of the Modern – World society 1815–1830* (HarperCollins: 1991)

Oxford Dictionary of Scientists (Oxford University Press: 1999)

Porter, R, *The Greatest Benefit to Mankind – A medical history of humanity* (WW Norton & Co: 1997)

Standage, T, *The Victorian Internet – The remarkable story of the telegraph and the nineteenth century's online pioneers* (Phoenix: 1999)

'The Electric Telegraph – Sir C Wheatstone's share in its invention', *The Scientific Review, and Journal of the Inventors' Institute*, 2 November 1868

www.acmi.net.au/AIC/phd8400.html
www.answers.com
www.bsip.com
www.chem.ch.huji.ac.il
www.cisi.unito.it
www.cwhistory.com
www.findagrave.com
www.history-world.org
www.iec.ch
www.ieee-virtual-museum.org
www.ilt.columbia.edu
www.juliantrubin.com
www.kcl.ac.uk
www.memory.loc.gov
www.si.edu
www.telegraph-history.org
www.telegraph-office.com
www.worldwideschool.org

4 Isaac Singer & the Sewing Machine

Oxford Illustrated Encyclopedia of Invention and Technology (Oxford University Press: 1992)

www.answers.com
www.cgazette.com
www.crazyweb.currantbun.com
www.historyofquilts.com
www.history.rochester.edu
www.husqvarnastudio.co.uk
www.inventors.about.com
www.ismacs.net
www.madehow.com
www.moah.org
www.netstate.com
www.rootswebancestry.com
www.scienceandsociety.co.uk
www.sew2go.com/smhistory.htm
www.sewalot.com
www.sewingmachinesguide.com
www.uh.edu

5 Charles Darwin & the Theory of Evolution

Bowler, PJ, *Charles Darwin – The man and his influence* (Cambridge University Press: 1996)
Burkhardt, RW, 'Lamarck, Evolution and the Politics of Science', *Journal of the History of Biology*, number 3, 1970

Burkhardt, RW, 'The Inspiration of Lamarck's Belief in Evolution', *Journal of the History of Biology*, number 5, 1972

Darwin, C, *The Origin of Species* (Gramercy: 1995)

Darwin, C, *The Descent of Man* (Prometheus Books: 1997)

Dobzhansky, T, 'Nothing in Biology Makes Sense except in the Light of Evolution', *The American Biology Teacher*, volume 35, March 1973

Gould, SJ, 'Evolution as Fact and Theory', *Discover*, May 1981

Lewontin, RC, 'Evolution/Creation Debate – A time for truth', *Bioscience*, volume 31, 1981

McKinney, H, *Lamarck to Darwin – Contributions to evolutionary biology, 1809–1859* (Coronado Press: 1971)

Wallace, AR, 'On the Tendency of Varieties to Depart Indefinitely from the Original Type' (London: 1858)

Zetterberg, JP (ed), *Evolution versus Creationism – The public education controversy* (Oryx Press: 1983)

www.crystalinks.com
www.evolution.berkeley.edu
www.pbs.org
www.talkorigins.org
www.ucmp.berkeley.edu
www.victorianweb.org
www.whonamedit.com
www.wku.edu

6 Thomas Crapper & the Flushing Toilet

Harington, Sir J (Donno, E, ed), *A New Discourse of a Stale Subject, Called the Metamorphosis of Ajax* (Routledge and Kegan Paul: 1962)

Hart-Davis, A, *Thunder, Flush and Thomas Crapper – An encyclopedia* (Trafalgar Square Publishing: 1997)

Juuti, P and Wallenius, K, *Brief History of Wells and Toilets* (Tampere University Press: 2005)

Mathé, J, *Le Invenzioni di Leonardo da Vinci* (Minerva: 1989)

Palmer, R, *The Water Closet – A new history* (David & Charles: 1973)

Reti, L and Dibner, B, *Leonardo da Vinci, Technologist* (Burndy Library: 1969)

Reyburn, W, *Flushed with Pride – The story of Thomas Crapper* (Trafalgar Square Publishing: 1991)

Williams, J (*et al*), *Leonardo da Vinci* (Horizon Caravel: 1965)

www.answers.com
www.bricksandbrass.co.uk
www.cs.uml.edu
www.exnet.com
www.hd.org
www.masterplumbers.com
www.muswell-hill.com
www.news.bbc.co.uk
www.nndb.com
www.plumbingsupply.com
www.theplumber.com
www.uh.edu
www.victoriancrapper.com

7 Richard Gatling, Sir Hiram Maxim & the Machine Gun

Mathé, J, *Le Invenzioni di Leonardo da Vinci* (Minerva: 1989)

Reti, L and Dibner, B, *Leonardo da Vinci, Technologist* (Burndy Library: 1969)

Williams, J (*et al*), *Leonardo da Vinci* (Horizon Caravel: 1965)

www.americanheritage.com
www.bbc.co.uk
www.bookrags.com
www.ccrkba.org
www.civilwar.bluegrass.net
www.encyclopedia.thefreedictionary.com
www.floridareenactorsonline.com
www.inventors.about.com
www.military.com
www.museoscienza.org
www.oldguns.net
www.open2.net
www.peninsulacampaign.org
www.reference.com
www.rochester-citynews.com
www.spartacus.schoolnet.co.uk
www.vintage-reprints.com
www.virginialighthorse.freeservers.com

8 Alexander Graham Bell & the Telephone

Aitken, W, *Who Invented the Telephone?* (Blackie and Son: 1939)

Baker, BH, *The Gray Matter – The forgotten story of the telephone* (Telepress: 2000)

Casson, HN, *The History of the Telephone* (AC McClurg & Co: 1910)

Coe, L, *The Telephone and Its Several Inventors – A history* (McFarland & Co: 1995)

Evenson, AE, *The Telephone Patent Conspiracy of 1876 – The Elisha Gray–Alexander Bell controversy and its many players* (McFarland & Co: 2000)

Grosvenor, ES and Wesson, M, *Alexander Graham Bell – The life and times of the man who invented the telephone* (Harry N Abrams: 1997)

Hounshell, DA, 'Two Paths to the Telephone', *Scientific American*, January 1981

McDougall, L, 'Official: Bell Didn't Invent the Telephone; "Top secret" file reveals that businessmen suppressed the identity of the telephone's real inventor', *Sunday Herald Online*, 23 November 2003

Schiavo, GE, *Antonio Meucci, Inventor of the Telephone* (Vigo Press: 1958)

Thompson, SP, *Philipp Reis, Inventor of the Telephone* (E & F Spon: 1883)

www.acmi.net.au
www.chem.ch.huji.ac.il
www.guardian.co.uk
www.ilt.columbia.edu
www.inventors.about.com

www.italianhistorical.org
www.juliantrubin.com
www.loc.gov
www.lucidcafe.com
www.oberlin.edu
www.obsolete.com
www.privateline.com
www.scitechantiques.com
www-stall.rz.fht-esslingen.de
www.who2.com

9 Thomas Edison & the Electric Light

Eisenman, HJ, *Charles F Brush – Pioneer innovator in electrical technology* (Case Institute of Technology: 1967)

Howell, JW and Schroeder, H, *History of the Incandescent Lamp* (The Maqua Company: 1927)

'Invention of the Incandescent Lamp', *Electrical World and Engineer*, volume 35, number 15, 14 April 1900

Lienhard, JH, *The Engines of our Ingenuity – An engineer looks at technology and culture* (Oxford University Press: 2003)

www.abc.net.au
www.answers.com
www.bergen.org
www.cc.columbia.edu
www.chem.ch.huji.ac.il
www.enchantedlearning.com
www.ideafinder.com

www.inventors.about.com
www.lafavre.us
www.lucidcafe.com
www.micro.magnet.fsu.edu
www.scienceworld.wolfram.com

10 Karl Benz & the Automobile

Mathé, J, *Le Invenzioni di Leonardo da Vinci* (Minerva: 1989)

Reti, L and Dibner, B, *Leonardo da Vinci, Technologist* (Burndy Library: 1969)

Williams, J (*et al*), *Leonardo da Vinci* (Horizon Caravel: 1965)

www.3wheelers.com
www.acs.bolton.ac.uk
www.arts.guardian.co.uk
www.brooklands.org.uk
www.citiesofscience.co.uk
www.cybersteering.com
www.history.rochester.edu
www.inventors.about.com
www.library.thinkquest.org
www.newadvent.org
www.news.bbc.co.uk
www.pages.zoom.co.uk/elvis/benz.html
www.quantium.plus.com
www.sapiensman.com
www.thehistoryof.net
www.uh.edu/engines

11 Guglielmo Marconi & the Radio

Anderson, LI, 'Priority in the Invention of Radio – Tesla vs Marconi', The Antique Wireless Association, monograph number 4, March 1980

Belrose, JS, 'Fessenden and Marconi – Their differing technologies and transatlantic experiments during the first decade of this century', International Conference on 100 Years of Radio, September 1995

Cheney, M, *Tesla – Man out of time* (Laurel Press: 1983)

'"Death Ray" for Planes', the *New York Times*, 22 September 1940

Garratt, GRM, *The Early History of Radio from Faraday to Marconi* (IEE Books: 1994)

Nichols, PB and Moon, P, *The Montauk Project – Experiments in time* (Sky Books: 1992)

'Nikola Tesla, Life and Work of a Genius', Yugoslavian Society for the Promotion of Scientific Thought, 1976

'Tesla's New Device like Bolts of Thor', the *New York Times*, 8 December 1915

Wunsch, AD, 'Misreading the Supreme Court – A puzzling chapter in the history of radio', *Antenna*, volume 11, November 1998

Zook, GE, 'Just Who Did Invent Radio?', *Amateur Radio Today*, number 73, July 1996

www.amasci.com
www.anomalyinfo.com
www.answers.com
www.crystalinks.com

www.edhelper.com
www.guardian.co.uk
www.inventors.about.com
www.juliantrubin.com
www.lucidcafe.com
www.mercurians.org
www.nobelprize.org
www.ntesla.org
www.oreillynet.com
www.pbs.org
www.qsl.net
www.sfmuseum.org
www.teslasociety.com
www.tfcbooks.com

12 Orville & Wilbur Wright & the Airplane

'An Air Navigator', *Scientific American*, volume 4, number 1, 23 September 1848

Gibbs-Smith, CH, *Clément Ader – His flight claims and his place in history* (HMSO: 1968)

'Is a Flying Machine a Mechanical Possibility?' *Scientific American*, volume 20, number 11, 13 March 1869

Lissarrague, P, *Clément Ader – Inventeur d'avions* (Bibliothèque Historique Privat: 1990)

Oxford Illustrated Encyclopedia of Invention and Technology (Oxford University Press: 1992)

Rodliffe, G, *Wings Over Waitohi – The story of Richard Pearse* (Avon Press: 1993)

Stewart, O, *Aviation – The creative ideas* (Frederick A Praeger: 1966)

www.af.mil/history
www.ba-education.com
www.centennialofflight.gov
www.chrisbrady.itgo.com
www.ctie.monash.edu.au
www.flyingmachines.org
www.karl-jatho.com
www.kidcyber.com.au
www.lucidcafe.com
www.news.bbc.co.uk

13 Henry Ford, Mass Production & the Assembly Line

Banham, R, *The Ford Century – Ford Motor Company and the innovations that shaped the world* (Artisan Press: 2002)

Brinkley, D, *Wheels for the World – Henry Ford, his company, and a century of progress, 1903–2003* (Penguin Books: 2003)

Giedon, S, *Mechanization Takes Command – A contribution to anonymous history* (Oxford University Press: 1948)

Green, CM, *Eli Whitney and the Birth of American Technology* (Little, Brown and Co: 1956)

Thompson, H, *The Age of Invention – A chronicle of mechanical conquest* (Yale University Press: 1921)

Tristram, P, 'Eli Whitney Started Spiral toward Sprawl with Fast Gun', *Daytona Beach News-Journal*, 12 August 2003

www.answers.com
www.bookrags.com
www.cottontimes.co.uk
www.ctheritage.org
www.echeat.com
www.engr.sjsu.edu
www.eyewitnesstohistory.com
www.ferdinando.org.uk
www.kidsnewsroom.org
www.michigan.gov
www.ryerson.ca
www.scielo.br
www.suite101.com
www.uh.edu/engines/epi1252.htm
www.u-s-history.com
www.yale.edu

14 James Watson, Francis Crick & the Discovery of DNA

Langridge, R, Wilson, HR, Hooper, CW, Wilkins, MHF and Hamilton, LD, 'The Molecular Configuration of Deoxyribonucleic Acid. I. X-ray diffraction study of a crystalline form of the lithium salt', *Journal of Molecular Biology*, volume 2, 1960

Maddox, B, *Rosalind Franklin – The dark Lady of DNA* (HarperCollins: 2002)

McMurray, EJ, *Notable Twentieth Century Scientists* (Thomson Gale: 1994)

Spencer, M, Fuller, W, Wilkins, MHF and Brown, GL, 'Determination of the Helical Configuration of

Ribonucleic Acid Molecules by X-ray Diffraction Study of Crystalline Amino-Acid-transfer Ribonucleic Acid', *Nature*, volume 194, 1962

Watson, JD, 'Thirty Years of DNA', *Nature*, volume 302, April 1983

Watson, JD and Crick, FHC, 'Genetical Implications of the Structure of Deoxyribonucleic Acid', *Nature*, volume 171, May 1953

www.answers.com
www.ba-education.com
www.chemheritage.org
www.exploratorium.edu
www.internetwks.com
www.library.thinkquest.org
www.mnsu.edu
www.news.bbc.co.uk
www.nobelprize.org
www.ornl.gov
www.pbs.org
www.rsnz.org